THE LADY
IN THE JUNGLE

THE LADY
IN THE JUNGLE

The Story of Mary Kingsley
in Africa

by Nelson Minier

MACRAE SMITH COMPANY: PHILADELPHIA

COPYRIGHT © 1961 BY NELSON MINIER

Library of Congress Catalogue Card Number 61-14955
Manufactured in the United States of America

6109

THE LADY
IN THE JUNGLE

CHAPTER ONE

DEW STILL GLISTENED ON THE GARDEN AND THE ROOFS OF neighboring houses although the sun had broken through the English morning mist. The world was so quiet that Mary's footsteps seemed to thunder on the gravel of the garden path. She looked back toward the house, a wary eye on the window of her father's study—and stumbled against the garden gate. Although she was only thirteen, and slim, the noise that resulted sounded to her ears like a blast that would bring her father storming to the window.

The window stayed shut and silent, however, and she went on. She was not doing anything wrong—in fact, she was trying to be on her best behavior—but Papa could not bear sudden, loud noises when he was writing or reading. Most of the time she could be as harum-scarum as she wished, because her father was away much of the time and Mama didn't mind. Now that Papa was home again, everything was different. The difference made Mary's heart thump with happy excitement as well as nervousness. It was better to have him home, even when he was angry with her, than far off in America or the West Indies or some other distant land.

"You mustn't pester your father with questions," her mother had warned her.

Mary sighed, bending down to smell the sweet, damp perfume of a clump of stocks. There was so much she wanted to know about those foreign lands, and about many other things, that it was almost impossible to be silent. The few books she had couldn't begin to give her the knowledge that Papa could. Perhaps tonight he would be in a mood to talk and tell stories about his adventures . . .

Something streaked past her, going toward the house, tail feathers and plumy crest breathing fire.

"Ki Ki!" Mary gasped. She picked up her skirt in one hand and started after the rooster, her fair hair streaming like the pet gamecock's tail feathers.

Ki Ki raced directly to the study window. There he stopped, one small, bright eye shining. He threw back his head, swelled up his chest inside the red cloth waistcoat Mary had made for him and yodeled triumphantly. The sound split the morning silence.

Mary winced and ducked behind a syringa bush.

The study window flew open and the powerful voice of Dr. George Kingsley ripped across the air. Gray eyes blazed in a sunburned face. Even the lines of his old velvet smoking jacket seemed to wrinkle in anger.

"You!" he shouted at Ki Ki. "Get out of here before I wring your noisy neck. Mary! Are you out there, Mary?"

Mary trembled and shrank back behind her bush. She waited. There was silence. Cautiously, she peeped around the bush. Her father and the rooster were glaring at each other, neither giving ground.

Finally Dr. Kingsley banged down the window.

"Ki Ki," Mary whispered pleadingly but Ki Ki was too busy preening himself in triumph to pay any attention. In another minute he would start a victory crow. Bending low, Mary crept toward him. If she could seize him and get him quietly out of earshot, the day might yet be saved.

She made a grab—and Ki Ki squawked outrageously.

Up went the window again with a crash. Mary ducked as a leather pouch came flying through the opening. A ruler whistled through the air. An inkwell plopped near the syringa bush behind which she had hid. With Ki Ki squawking under her arm, she reached up and caught a carved letter opener that came spinning toward her.

She was almost beyond range of the flying objects when a book came fluttering through the air and landed in front of her. She bent and scooped it up. It was the familiar Johnson's *Robberies and Murders of the Most Notorious Pyrates*, which she knew almost by heart. Papa should not have thrown that one; it was one of the best books in the house.

"Mary!"

She turned. Her father was leaning out of the study window, looking grimly down at her.

"Yes, Papa."

"How many times have I told you to keep that stupid bird away from the house? Why your mother permits you to keep those creatures as pets I'll never understand."

Because she likes pets, too, Mary wanted to answer, but it seemed safer to keep still. "I tried to lock Ki Ki up," she said, apology in her blue eyes. "I built a new pen myself."

The look on her father's face suggested that no girl knew anything about carpentry or should even try to know. Mary knew the look well. It was the same look that met her when she timidly mentioned wanting to learn mathematics or languages. Once, at her dreamiest, she had even thought of studying medicine and becoming a successful doctor like her father. The truth was, she would be lucky if she learned simple nursing. There were great plans for her young brother Charles' education, but neither Papa nor Mama felt that girls needed to learn much more than how to sew and keep house and wait on the men of the family.

"Come into the house," her father ordered. "And bring that book in with you."

"Yes, Papa." She hurried off to put Ki Ki back in his pen, scolding him, and pushing a stone against the board he had loosened in his escape.

Her mother was in the kitchen, helping Mrs. Barrett, the hired woman, to prepare breakfast.

"Your father wants you in the study, Mary," she said. "Your sash is all undone, and your hair looks like a feather duster. What have you been up to?"

Mary held up the book. "Papa . . . uh . . . lost this out the window. He wants me to bring it to him." Her eyes twinkled at her mother.

Mrs. Kingsley permitted a faint smile to appear on her face, but at a noise from the kitchen it changed to a frown. "Mrs. Barrett, please," she called, "can't you make less noise with those pans? Mary, be sure and tell the gardener not to do any pounding today . . . and have somebody grease the pump handle again. It still squeaks." Her fingers worked at Mary's sash as she spoke.

Impatient to reach her father's study, Mary sighed. Bows were tiresome things. She wondered if Queen Victoria had ever worn such fussy ribbons when she was young. The Queen always seemed so sensible.

Her mother said, "Tell your father we are having breakfast on the terrace, as the day is turning out so pleasant. And then go up and tell Charles I'll send breakfast up to him. Poor boy, his cold seems worse again. And just at the start of school holidays, too."

We are not a very rugged family, Mary thought as she went toward the study. Charles had never been strong, and Mama often had nervous headaches. She had headaches herself more often than she let her mother know. Papa was the only strong one, going on one rough adventure after another. She knocked at his door, hoping he was over the worst of his wrath against her and Ki Ki.

"Who is it?" Dr. Kingsley called.

"It's only me, Papa."

"Come in, come in. There's no sense standing there half the day."

Mary opened the door and walked across the polished boards of the floor. Pleasant odors of pipe smoke and leather and the strange, sweet dry smell of books wafted to her. She loved the study with its collections of arrows and South Sea masks, hunting knives, and strange souvenirs of exotic places, more than anything else at Southwood Lane. And the garden. Those, and her father's being home, turned Highgate into a place of magic instead of the ordinary London neighborhood it was.

Her father turned in his chair to look at her. "Good morning, Miss Mary."

She gave him a quick, alert glance and saw that the anger was gone from his face. There was a sparkle of amusement now in his eyes; his lips, under the moustache, were even curving into a smile.

"Good morning, Papa. I hope you slept well." She put the book about pirates down and glanced over his shoulder at a current periodical he was reading. The article, dated June, 1875, was about American Indians in the West. A dozen questions tumbled through her mind but she did not feel quite bold enough to ask them. Her father had gone with Lord Dunraven, as the lord's personal physician, on a trip to America. They had been there nearly two years, had traveled through the wilderness with the famous American scout Buffalo Bill, had helped fight a prairie fire, and had hunted and fished over the entire continent. Remembering some of the things Papa had told her and Charles about his adventures, she grew braver. "Tell me again what Buffalo Bill looked like, Papa," she coaxed.

Dr. Kingsley leaned back in his chair, looking out at the garden as if he were once more gazing out over the western plains of America. He described the famous scout's appearance—the silky beard, the long hair, and the flame in his eyes when he was chasing game. Then he said, "Now that's enough of that. I've discovered some new material on early South American tribes." He lifted a sheaf of papers. "I could use a secretary after breakfast, if your mother can spare you."

"I'll ask her right away." Mary hurried out, her face glowing. While Papa was away, she had arranged his scientific journals in the order of their topics, and she had used every spare minute left over from her household tasks in making notes on the subjects that particularly interested her father, like early religions and tribal law. He would be pleased with what she had done.

She went to the terrace to find her mother putting the finishing touches to the breakfast table.

"Of course, if your father needs you," Mrs. Kingsley assured Mary, "you're excused from other duties."

There was a shout from the direction of the garden: "Something's in the la-a-ane!"

From the kitchen came Mrs. Barrett's echoing cry, "Something's in the lane!"

Dr. Kingsley burst from his study. "Now what? Is there never any peace and quiet around this house?"

The gardener's boy raced past the terrace and vaulted over the low boundary hedge, yelling, "It's Trenton's cattle again! I'll get the dogs . . ."

"Keep the dogs out of the garden!" Dr. Kingsley shouted, going to help with the chase.

When he finally returned, the lane cleared of cattle, he panted, "That lane! It will be the death of me."

"More likely it will be the death of us," Mary retorted. She had spent many a morning chasing cows or pigs or strange dogs. One night her mother had even taken a revolver out to scare away a prowler. A lot Papa knew about their troubles with the lane when he was halfway around the world.

Her father gave her a sharp glance, then dropped, panting, into one of the terrace chairs. "There's a little stiffness in my knee. I'll have to have one of my colleagues look at it before I start on my next trip."

"Your next—but you've been home only a few days!" Mrs. Kingsley exclaimed, the shadows under her eyes seeming to deepen.

George Kingsley waved his hand. "I'm not going immediately, dear. I expect to be home for months. Now let's all sit down and try to relax and enjoy breakfast."

As they ate, Mary stole glances at her father's face. Restlessness was already evident. With a sinking heart, she knew that he would soon be off.

"By the way," he said when they were almost through with the meal, turning to Mary, "I noticed you put my journals in order, Mary."

Pleasure and pride welled up in Mary's heart—but it was followed by sharp realization. No matter how hard she might work or study, trying to ferret knowledge from books, he would never expect or even want her to be more than a sometimes secretary, or a helper around the house.

As if he sensed her thoughts her father reached over and patted her hand, adding, "A good job, too, Miss Mary."

"Thank you, Papa." She looked down at her lap. After all, what worthier life could there be than that of helping the people one loved? It was wilful and ungrateful of her to yearn for more. Smothering a sigh, she made up her mind to try to be content with what she had—books and her game-cocks and a chance to work with her father.

The front door knocker sounded one morning while Mary and her father were working over his notes on tools and weapons used by Canadian Indian tribes. Reluctantly Dr. Kingsley put aside his pen, but when he saw who his visitor was, a warm smile came to his face.

The visitor was Dr. Oakeshott, one of his best friends. Waving the doctor to a chair, Mary's father told her to go ahead copying the notes he had given her.

"I brought back some of that gunpowder I wrote you of," he told Dr. Oakeshott. Opening one of his packing cases, he brought out a tin box. "I'll give you a sample, but be careful. Use much less than you do of the regular kind."

Mary listened. Mama had been complaining about the unsightly oak roots left in the yard when a tree had blown down in a storm. It seemed to her that this powerful new gunpowder would be just the thing to use to get rid of them.

Several mornings later, when Dr. Kingsley was out, Mary took a sample of the gunpowder in a little box out to the yard and wedged the box firmly among the oak roots. She had attached a wick long enough to give her time to get clear of the spot before the powder exploded.

Mary was ready to strike a match to the fuse when she heard Mrs. Barrett come outside to the small back yard. She waited until she heard the woman go back indoors and then quickly lit her homemade fuse, running around a corner of the house as fast as she could, afterward.

Boom!

A shudder of triumph and alarm went down Mary's spine.

"Eeeek!" a voice wailed. "The clothes!" Mrs. Barrett came running from the house at the same time that Mary rounded the corner.

There hung the washing Mrs. Barrett had just fastened to the clothesline—spattered with large brown spots!

Mary stared at the spots, then at the shattered oak roots. "Wh-what made those spots?"

Pale and shaken, Mrs. Barrett pointed a wrathful finger. "Manure, that's what! The gardener had a tubful sitting here . . . Whatever were you doing, anyway? I thought there'd been an earthquake."

There might as well have been, Mary thought, looking with horrified chagrin at the tub sitting near the dahlia bed. It was still half full of rich, brown liquid. The other half of the liquid was dripping from the once-clean clothes.

"I was—experimenting," she said weakly.

"Experimenting!" Mrs. Barrett's mouth still hung open and she looked as if the end of the world had come with a blast of trumpets. "You could have blown us all up."

That night, after her father came home and was told about Mary's "experiment," she received a stern lecture. Not only was it exceedingly stupid of her to treat dynamite as though it were some sort of toy, but she had been wicked, too, for taking the gunpowder in the first place. "You had no business in my study this morning," Dr. Kingsley scolded.

For once, Mary's mother put in a word. "*You* have no

business bringing those terrible explosives into the house," she said to her husband.

In the argument between them which followed, Mary escaped to her own room. She lit a lamp and looked in the bedroom mirror at her plain, strong-jawed face. The lamp-light flickered over the steady cheekbones, lighting up her fair hair and bright blue eyes. She really had been both wicked and stupid, she supposed. A sudden memory of Mrs. Barrett's face, however, brought a dimple flashing at the corner of her mouth. Wait until I tell Charley how she looked when she saw that washing, Mary thought. Her brother had gone back to school the day before but would be home again in a week. She hoped he would bring all his books with him when he came because Papa wanted her to begin to study German. She would need it, he said, for some of the jobs he wanted her to do in connection with his work.

✿ CHAPTER TWO

SUNLIGHT CAME THROUGH THE WINDOW OF THE HOUSE IN Bexley Heath in North Kent, illuminating the pages of the magazine Mary Kingsley held. The magazine was called *The English Mechanic*. She studied the page before her, then looked out at the coach house and the new neighborhood to which she and her family had moved. She was eighteen now, old enough to be responsible for most of the household affairs. The Kingsleys no longer had a regular housekeeper because having too many people around made Mary's mother nervous. The family had moved to Kent in the hope that its drier climate would improve Mama's health, which had been growing steadily worse at Highgate.

Mary stood up, smoothing her skirt. Maybe the climate was dry, but the ceiling over the coach house definitely was not. With Charles either sick or away at school most of the time, and Papa wandering around in his beloved jungles, and Mama frail as a matchstick, and handymen so expensive it seemed their fingers were made of gold, there was only one person around to do something about the leaking pipe in the coach house. With her long skirt swishing around her boot tops, Mary went to assemble the tools for the job, calling to Dick, the odd job boy, at the same time.

A few moments later, she was standing on a box in the

coach house, her sleeves rolled up, eyeing the faulty ceiling where an exposed, leaky pipe challenged her ingenuity. "Hand me the saw, Dick," she commanded the boy beside her. "It's really a simple job," she added, to bolster her own confidence, "once you have the hang of it." She did not mention that *The English Mechanic*, a few issues back, had explained just how to go about such a chore, but went on to declare authoritatively, "You simply cut the pipe through, then double it back and hammer it up neatly again." Mary felt quite sure that was how the magazine article had said to go about it.

Dick's round face wore a doubtful look. "You'd best let a man handle that."

"Nonsense. You know nothing at all about it."

"Yes, mum." Sullenly, the boy handed her the tool.

As Mary attacked the lead pipe with vigor, she reminded herself that plumbing was no different basically from other mechanical tasks, and she had tackled plenty of them. Hardly a week passed when there wasn't some kind of mending job—a broken latch, a splintered window sash, or an ailing door hinge.

The pipe was tougher than she had expected. A bead of perspiration leaked down from under the braids circling her head. Nervousness made her throat faintly dry. Whatever happened, she was not going to cry for help from that sneering boy.

"Just about through," she proclaimed cheerfully. "Simple enough, as I said——"

A jet of water shot from the pipe, whooshing into her face and eyes with such force that Mary reeled backward. The box tipped. Over she went, onto the floor, the hard stream of water drenching her.

Dick burst into a wild guffaw. "Ho, ho, miss, you've let loose a flood!"

Mary's cheeks flamed. She struggled to her feet, her wet hair straggling down around her face, her skirt and blouse dripping. "Go turn off the water, you idiot!" she sputtered, coughing against the water she had swallowed. She wrung out her skirt and then ran for a broom; water was pouring all over the floor.

Still doubled over with laughter, Dick ran for the water main. Mary swept at the water vigorously, trying to sweep it through the door, but it was like sweeping a river. If that stupid boy didn't hurry . . .

The water stopped flowing and Dick returned to stand grinning at her.

Mary, her own lips quivering with laughter, said with an attempt at sternness, "There's nothing so amusing about it. Put the box back and we'll finish the job."

"Yes, Miss Mary." Dick gave her a sidelong glance which was still so full of suppressed mirth that Mary's own sense of humor overcame her. The two of them began to laugh. They laughed so hard that they were almost too weak to finish the job.

When they had finished, Mary brushed her damp hands together and commented, "This has been an example, Dick, of the pursuit of knowledge under difficulties."

He gave her a blank look. He could scarcely know about the book *Pursuit of Knowledge Under Difficulties*, which Papa and Mama had given her when she complained about not having a chance to learn about chemistry and other sciences. She ought to have had common sense enough to turn off the water before tinkering with plumbing, or what was the use of having technical knowledge?

In the house, Mary heard her mother call to her as she

went upstairs to her room. "I'll be back down in a minute, Mama," she called back. If Mama saw her in her present drenched condition she would be alarmed. Everything worried her mother these days. She had always been nervous and high-strung but now she seemed stretched so thin that anything might make her snap. Papa had been due home a month ago but changes of plan along the way kept his arrival indefinite. If he only realized how hard the suspense was, Mary thought as she dried her hair and swiftly pinned it up again. Still, she couldn't blame him for wanting to have all the adventures he could, on his travels. Papa was not, she told herself in a burst of defensive pride, like other, less exciting husbands and fathers. He believed it was his role in life to go off hunting and shooting in wild places, as he felt it was her mother's role to keep the house together while he was away. As for herself, her particular job was to do whatever jobs were at hand to be done, whether it was scrubbing floors or keeping her father's journals in order.

She let herself bask for a few minutes in the satisfaction she felt from being a background helper in the world of science and exploration. Students, explorers, hunters, adventurers of all kinds, were the most exciting people in the world. Putting her own thin, pale image beside that of her father's bold, strong one, she sighed. Papa was a regular treasure house of knowledge and when he was home, some of the most brilliant men in the scientific world came to see him. Mary felt a familiar tide of melancholy and depression arising from a sense of her own worthlessness. No matter what she tried to do in the way of helping Papa, it seemed so feeble and inadequate.

Her mother was calling again, this time impatiently.

Mary shook off her brooding thoughts and went quickly

downstairs and into the parlor where her mother lay on a couch.

"What is it, Mama?"

Her mother's cheeks were pink and her eyes bright, but not with fever. "Your father's coming home! Here." She held a letter out. "He's in Devon. He'll be here in a day or two."

Mary took the letter with soaring spirits. "Oh!" she exclaimed when she had read it, "that's wonderful news." She bent down and hugged her mother and then stood up, her mind whirling in happy confusion as she tried to decide what to do first in preparation for her father's return. A list of instructions for the day servant, Hetty, formed in her mind. "I'll tell Hetty to order some fish. Papa always wants fish when he comes home."

Her mother smiled. "Sit down and calm yourself, Mary. There's another letter here. Your cousins have sent you an invitation to a house party next week."

"Whatever for?" Mary, frowning, dropped onto a stool beside her mother's couch. "I shall certainly not go, with Papa home. I'll write at once and refuse—and I'll write to Charley, too, so he can arrange a holiday while Papa's here." She was not a bit of use at a party and she hated having to get all dressed up to go and be puss-in-the-corner. "Would you like a coddled egg, Mamma?"

"Anything will taste good now, dear."

Mary went to the kitchen, glad that her mother was already feeling better. After she had prepared Mama's egg, she must give Hetty orders. Today's would be the last thorough cleaning the place would get for some time, with her father home. Rug-beating drove him into a frenzy.

For Mary, the prospect of giving all the rugs a fine, vigorous beating seemed a delightful way to get rid of the excitement humming in her. She sang a snatch of an old song that Papa had started teaching her back at Southgate, a song he had learned from Buffalo Bill. He had refused to teach her the whole song because, he said, it was not fit for a lady.

Not even for a lady plumber, she supposed, smiling to herself.

There were never such wonderful times as when Mary's father came home with packing cases full of curios and his mind and conversation spiced with his adventures. The household changed tempo. Mama, Mary thought, was almost vivacious, and her brother Charley wittier and bubbling with great plans for the future. Charley, too, wanted to travel, he said, although his sister could never quite fit his milder, more delicate personality into the life of adventure her father described to them. She hung on her father's every word, wore herself out waiting on him, and eavesdropped when she could on the talk between him and his distinguished visitors. Sometimes, when he and she were alone, she told him about some of her own adventures with leaking pipes and stubborn window sills.

The sweet excitement of her husband's homecoming was almost too much for Mrs. Kingsley. The morning after Dr. Kingsley's arrival from Devon, she did not come down to breakfast. Charles, too, was worn out from the lateness of the hour when they had all gone to bed, and was sleeping as long as he could. Mary, alone with her father, saw to it that his tea was hot and strong and the eggs done exactly as he liked them. Outside, the September day was gray except for handfuls of colored leaves which dropped to the ground from time to time. The spinning leaves seemed to weave bright, moving walls around the house, adding to the wonderful sense of luxury she felt: she and Papa together, with time to talk.

"More bacon?" she urged him.

"No, no more, thank you, Mary." He leaned back in his chair and lit his pipe, studying her. His look was keen and she felt suddenly as if she were a representative of a strange tribe he had come to study and evaluate. Had he found the translations she had so painfully made of an article, written in German, on ancient Egyptian sun worship?

"You're getting to be a fine homemaker," he said. "I suppose some young man has been hanging around and you have been practicing the domestic arts with the future in mind."

She answered with a quick, self-mocking smile, "If so, it's a future nobody seems especially eager to share." The young men she knew were polite enough and sometimes, at parties, one of them sat and talked to her about books or cricket or some other safe topic, but none ever asked to call on her. Perhaps she was too timid or perhaps she didn't choose things to talk about that interested them. Her lip twitched at a sudden memory of the young man at her cousin Rose's house, to whom she had recited whole paragraphs from Burton's *Anatomy of Melancholy*. He had looked very unhappy and had seized the first excuse to leave her. This inability to interest young men made her feel mildly sad sometimes, because it was obvious that she was missing something wonderful in life, but she never felt desperate about it. There was so much inside her head, and so much work to do right there at home, that she was too busy to have time for self-pity. The dark melancholy she did often feel came from something deeper, something she did not herself understand.

"Well," her father said, recalling Mary's wandering

thoughts abruptly, "you have years ahead of you for marriage. Right now your mother needs you." He blew a great cloud of smoke into the air. "One of these days I trust Charley will find more time for studies in the fields I want him to concentrate on." He rubbed his forefinger thoughtfully back and forth under his mustache. "I won't live forever. It's a great solace to have a son to carry on one's work."

"Yes," Mary said, thinking of the manuscripts in the study dealing with all kinds of obscure learning, although chiefly on early English literature and Semitic tradition. "They should all be published, Papa, those papers of yours. I've found some new accounts, in a German book, on sacrificial rites and copied them out for you . . ."

"Have you?" His eyes lit with sharp interest.

For a glorious half hour they talked of his work and of Mary's contributions to it. "You'll have to have help with your German, now," he said. "You've gone as far as you can by yourself. We'll get you a tutor." He stood up. "I must go up and see how your mother is. You might as well start unpacking my boxes. Get that boy, whatever his name is, to help you."

A private tutor for German! Mary was too surprised to take it in. She had never had any sort of teacher, except Papa himself, in her life. Her anticipation, and her delight that she was going to be permitted to unpack her father's treasures, sent her mind spinning like the leaves. It was almost worth having Papa go away, to share a homecoming like this one.

That evening Mary was still unpacking the crates and parcels and wonderfully mysterious cartons of her father's luggage. As she removed each new item from its container, she had to force herself to put it aside and go on to the

24

next. Books tumbled about her. She had not read a new book since her friend Anne Martin's father had loaned her *Variations of Plants and Animals Under Domestication* by Charles Darwin. She must remember to ask Papa what he thought of Darwin's book; she thought it wonderful herself. She picked the top book off the pile beside her, and in spite of the waning light, opened it and began to read.

She was still reading, straining her eyes against the dusk, when her father came in. She put the book down hastily.

"Not done yet?" he asked, looking around at the confusion and the unopened boxes. "And such gloom. I'm expecting Dr. Evans to drop around, so will you please light the lamp, Mary?"

She got to her feet and had just turned up the wick when her father's friend arrived.

"Go on with your work, Mary," her father said, "but be as quiet as you can."

Mary took a few of the books off a chair and made room for the visitor to sit down, before retiring to the book shelves to try to find room there for the new volumes. Behind her, the two men plunged into a discussion ranging over a vast field: tropical fish, the use of herbs in early medicine, the variety of ferns her father had found in the Devonshire woods . . . As Mary worked, she listened, and the time went all too swiftly. When she had finished with the books and other items from the open cases, she sat down by a hassock near the window, to watch the stars.

As the visitor finally got up to leave, Mary's father picked up the book Mary had put down when he came in. "Here, Evans—just what I wanted to show you. This work of Lockyer's on *Solar Physics* is absolutely fascinating. I've not quite finished it but when I have I'll send it over to you."

Mary caught her lower lip between her teeth to keep from protesting, "But *I* haven't finished it yet!" Stubbornness rose in her, and the normally quiet-looking eyes flashed.

"It's time you were in bed," Dr. Kingsley said when he returned from seeing his guest to the door. "I'll read awhile." As he picked up the Lockyer book and began to read Mary noticed that he had very few pages left. He would surely finish it tonight.

A peep into her mother's room told her that the semi-invalid was asleep. Gently, Mary closed the door again.

In her own room, she changed into her nightgown, took Bayle's *Dictionary* from its shelf, and tried to lose herself in its familiar pages. Tonight the old charm was missing. All of her attention was fixed on the study downstairs and the faint glow of the study lamp where it shone out against a plane tree.

She blew her candle out and waited. After what seemed forever, she heard her father's footsteps go past her door to his own room. When all sounds ceased, she stole quietly out of her room, her heart thumping. At the bottom of the stairs she paused, thinking she heard an upstairs door open. Nothing happened and she moved on, the starlight dimly lighting her way. *Solar Physics* was still on her father's desk and Mary's fingers closed eagerly over the book.

The next morning, she was sweeping leaves from the porch when her father came out, his face stormy.

"Did you take a book from my study without permission?"

Mary moved her broom lightly across the weathered boards. "A book?" she asked innocently.

"Yes, a book! Did you or did you not remove Lockyer's book on physics from my desk early this morning?"

The clock had not struck midnight when she stole down

the stairs, Mary remembered. She could truthfully say that she had not taken the book this morning. "No, Papa."

He frowned, suspicion and bewilderment on his sun-browned face, but he finally went back to his study. As soon as he was gone, Mary put down her broom and ran toward a shed at the rear of the garden.

Solar Physics was where she had hidden it, under a pile of straw in the corner of the shed. She drew it out, found a sheltered spot, and began to read swiftly, hungrily. Dr. Evans would get the book as soon as she was done with it.

✣ CHAPTER THREE

"DON'T WALK SO FAST, CHARLEY. I DO WANT TO HAVE A LOOK at everything." Mary Kingsley put a restraining hand on her brother's gowned sleeve as they walked past Emanuel College and then down Christ's Lane. Everything in Cambridge was so fascinating to Mary that she felt like stopping to study every stone in every building. Even the air seemed different here, as if the spirits of John Milton and Darwin and the other famous scholars who had attended the University lingered in the air.

Charles slowed his pace, pointing out objects of interest, although he glanced at his watch once or twice.

Her brother had no idea how lucky he was to be a law student in Christ's college, Mary thought. She could only stand hungrily outside the historic walls, dreaming of the knowledge stored in the books of the library and in the minds of the University's great teachers. Girls were not sent to school in England in 1883. Still, it was wonderful to be in Cambridge where there was so much of intellectual value around her.

"We must get back soon," Charles said, pulling his watch from his pocket. "I have an appointment in an hour."

"All right." With a lingering glance at the towers and courts, Mary took her brother's arm and they headed homeward.

Dr. Kingsley was waiting for them with his usual impatience when they got back to the house in Mortimer Road overlooking Parker's Piece, where the family was living while Charles was in college.

"I'm going over to the river to watch the rowing," Dr. Kingsley told Mary.

"You ought to keep away from the river, Papa. That damp air makes your rheumatism worse."

"Do you expect me to retire to a bench just because my legs are a bit stiff?" he retorted.

"Well, don't blame me if you come home limping."

"I'll walk along with you for a block or so," Charles told his father, "since we're headed somewhat the same way."

The two men left and Mary watched their departure from a front window. Overhead the sky was gray and dull —as gray and dull as her own life. She felt let down after the stimulation of exploring the University campus. Between watching over her father, nursing her invalid mother, running the household efficiently and trying to help her father with his research, she was being used up and worn out, without ever having really lived. She yearned for something unknown and undefined, something to give color and significance to her life.

The room was chilly. Mary turned from the window, shivering, and went to make the fire. Probably her fit of melancholy was only the Kingsley blood yearning for tropical lands and sunshine.

Behind her, a wall clock ticked loudly, a steady, small rhythm.

Twenty-one, twenty-one, twenty-one, it seemed to say. You are twenty-one, twenty-one . . .

Mary sighed. She removed her bonnet and tucked up some wisps of hair that had worked loose from their confining hairpins.

Her mother called from her room above and Mary went to see what the sick woman wanted.

Sometimes Mary did not hear the clock's steady ticking. Sometimes she heard only her mother moaning in her sleep, or the sound of the roof creaking under a winter storm. Sometimes, in spring, she listened to the wildly caroling birds as they flew from here to there, from there to here, and wished for a moment that she had been born a bird.

Heard or unheard, the clock ticked on: Twenty-two, twenty-three, twenty-four, swallowing up the minutes, the days, the hours. Twenty-five, twenty-six . . .

One break came in the monotony of her days when a friend of Mary's father, Miss Lucy Toulmin-Smith, took Mary on a trip to Paris—but she came back to find things at home even worse than when she left. Her father's rheumatism grew worse and worse and rheumatic fever had left him with a damaged heart. A trip around the world, intended to improve his health, was a failure. He returned home to become another claimant for his daughter's nursing care.

One morning in early February, 1892, Mary opened her eyes to see pale light filtering through the kitchen windows. She had been up most of the night, sitting beside her mother's bed because the sick woman was restless, and she had overslept. It was late. She started up nervously and hurried downstairs to make morning tea for both of her parents.

Hearing the postman, she went to get the mail before taking up her father's tray. He liked to have his letters as soon as he was awake. She saw, as she glanced through the mail, that there was a letter from Dr. Günther of the

British Museum. Papa would be happy to get that one. He thought very highly of the director of the Museum.

On her way, Mary peered in at her mother but Mrs. Kingsley was still asleep. A good thing, too, Mary thought, closing the door again softly, after such a bad night.

She knocked lightly on the door of the adjoining room, and said, "It's me. The post has been."

There was no answer.

She knocked again, more loudly, but fear was already creeping into her heart. From below came the great gonging stroke of the clock but there was still no sound from her father.

She pushed the door open, her heart beating almost as loud as the pendulum of the clock, and looked toward the bed. The motionlessness of the figure lying there told her that what she had feared was true. Her father was dead.

She set down the tray and crossed the room, staring down at the still features, one hand holding her slender throat as if to choke off a rasping sob that threatened. After a moment, she turned away and stumbled toward the next room. Her mother would have to be wakened and told the dreadful news.

Six weeks later, Mrs. Kingsley followed her husband. She had kept alive for his homecomings; with his death, nothing could hold her to life.

The clock still ticked but now it was a background to an increasingly meaningless swish of dustcloth or broom. Mary kept busy to keep away ghosts.

A good job, Mary . . . By the bye, bring me that article . . . Light the lamp, Mary . . . Bring me my pipe . . .

And the other, more fretful voice: *Mary dear, another pillow, this one's so hot . . . a fresh glass of water, please . . .*

When Charles was home, Mary tried to be cheerful but once she burst out, "I can't stand it, Charley! There's nothing for me to do!"

Her brother looked at his older sister in alarm. "Do?" he asked. "What do other girls do, who don't have parents to worry about?"

Charles was a man—he did not understand, Mary thought in despair. The late spring rain pounded against the garden, streaming from the gutters. Sometimes at night, the wind in the eaves sounded like wind in a ship's rigging; it seemed to be calling to her.

She stared at her image in the mirror. Surely there was something, somewhere . . . South America? China? Africa? The West Indies?

Her old friend the wall clock ticked at her back. Thirty, it said. You are thirty, thirty . . . too late, too alone, too ignorant, too helpless . . .

She moved about the house, waiting, listening. A horse-drawn cab rattled past outside. Perhaps her father's friend, Dr. Henry Guillemard, would drop by to visit with her as he used to with her father. The cab went on. No one stopped. She was alone with the rain and the flickering fire.

She stirred the fire and watched the sparks rise. New warmth reached out to her and the cold in the core of her bones melted away. She thought of tropical suns and fastened her mind on a distant light and hope. Eagerly she brought out her father's maps. A steady finger moved exploringly over oceans and coast lines and travel routes. Across from the colored dots representing the Canary Islands, on one of the maps, lay the great hulk of Africa. She sat absorbed, her finger on the dots, letting the gray English dusk take over the room while her mind filled with an exciting dream.

personal love for the sea, for trees and gnarled roots, for swamps and clouds, than she was able to feel for more than a very few human individuals.

Seeing the look on her face, the same look she had worn back in the days when she tackled a leaky pipe or wedged dynamite under the tree roots, her brother sighed and waved his hand. "It's clear I can't stop you once you've made up your mind, so I won't try."

It was some time before Charles left on his own travels but as soon as he was gone, Mary made her plans. Others besides Charles would think she was crazy unless she could offer some simple, obvious reason for going to Africa. She was not equipped to be a trader, the main occupation of most English citizens on the coast, nor was she the wife of a missionary or a government official. What she needed was some scientific backing and approval. Perhaps her father's old friend, Dr. Guillemard, at Cambridge, would help her.

Dr. Guillemard's reaction to her plan, the day that Mary visited him in his study, was as astonished as her brother's had been. She listened quietly to the same warnings and fears. "You are surely not serious about this," Guillemard finished. His eyes searched her face. "Yes, I see that you are. But, what would you do there?"

"That's why I'm here. If you could arrange some small scientific mission for me, some official job, it would make it easier for me to explain to the traders and officials out there why I came." She looked down at her gloved hands. "I know I lack true scientific training, but I've done a great deal of research. And I'm interested in every branch of knowledge." Humility and hope and despair mingled in her voice. "Most of all, I want to do something—find a reason for living."

Dr. Guillemard shifted the papers on his desk. He knew

the burdens his visitor had borne almost alone for many years and he sympathized with her driving need for work to do. He said finally, "Well, since I can't talk you out of going, we had better find a job for you. Perhaps Dr. Günther will have something he wants collected. Will you have enough funds?"

"I have five hundred pounds a year."

Five hundred pounds was something over two thousand dollars. Not too much to cover traveling expenses and provide the equipment necessary to make a collection for the British Museum, Dr. Guillemard said.

"I've had to learn how to make do with a shilling when a pound is asked for," Mary reminded him, with a half-smile.

As her brother had done, Dr. Guillemard recognized the strength of Mary's determination, and said he would get in touch with the Museum director at once.

The task that Dr. Günther found for Mary was to collect fishes and insects in Africa. No money would be forthcoming to help her with the assignment, Dr. Günther explained with apologies, but if it was authorization she wanted, she had it.

Mary now had a respectable excuse for going to Africa. Equipment for her task, glass containers for the fish specimens, cartons and mounting papers for insects, alcohol for preserving the fish, nets and other items would be both expensive and difficult to transport, but Mary felt nothing but satisfaction and anticipation when she walked away from her interview at the Museum.

The remainder of the winter of 1893 was spent in reading everything she could lay her hands on, about the dark and distant rivers of Africa. Her mind buzzed with facts about ichthyology and entomology, which she needed for

36

the Museum task. Her other task—the one she had set herself, of learning to know and understand the ways of the native people—she was already partially prepared for, but she continued to dig into her father's papers and whatever books covering the subject she could find. Remembering that Africa had practically no trained medical men or women, she went to Germany to take a short course in nursing to add to the practical knowledge she had acquired in the years she was her mother's sole nurse.

Like her brother, Mary's friends were horrified when they learned of her plans. One, a doctor friend of her father's who had spent seven years in West Africa, showed Mary a world map. "Look here," he said, pointing to the African west coast, "this map shows the distribution of killing diseases around the world. Do you see the color of West Africa, from above Sierra Leone to below the Congo, where you say you want to go? It's black. Black on this map has nothing to do with the skin color of the people who live there. It simply means that right there is the greatest concentration of deadly disease anywhere in the world. Now Scotland's a good, healthy country with lots of fish to be found in its rivers. Why don't you go study the fishes of Scotland?"

"I'm going to Africa," Mary said quietly.

The doctor let out an exasperated breath. "All right, then. If you must go, here are a few rules. First, don't get out under the direct rays of the sun. Second, take four grains of quinine every day for two weeks before you reach the river country. Last—and probably most important—try to make friends with the Methodist missionaries. They're the only ones out there who have a hearse with plumes on it. I'd like to make sure you'll be buried in style."

Mary laughed. "I'll just have to make do with whatever

cart is available, when the time comes. Chances are I'll not be asked to walk to my own funeral, even in Africa."

Joking about the danger did not mean that Mary had no apprehensions of her own. Packing her luggage after Charles had left, she wondered if she would ever return to this place that held her father's books and treasures. She might never again see her brother.

She thrust an umbrella into a long, waterproof bag that closed at the top with a bar and handle, driving away her anxiety in action. If Africa was going to kill her, it would, but at least she would first have done a small bit of living.

With the umbrella she stowed an extra portion of quinine, gift of a friend at the last minute. She didn't really want to die, she told herself, and she would certainly take all the precautions possible to prevent such a disaster. She intended to be very sensible and take care of her health as much as she could.

One item remained to be packed: Charley's old trousers. A pair of trousers under her skirts might prove extremely practical in rough country even though she considered them too unfeminine to be her visible costume.

Last of all, she closed the bag containing her scientific equipment, her mind leaping ahead, beyond fears and practical details, to the adventures she hoped to have. This was how her father must have felt at the start of every journey, she thought, feeling a renewal of identification with him. It was almost as though she were her father, for one brief moment . . . Tears pricked her eyelids but she refused to let them fall. Grief had had its day. The time had come for Mary Kingsley to look ahead.

CHAPTER FOUR

LIVERPOOL WAS A BUSTLE OF SHIPS AND SAILORS AND EMBARK-
ing passengers. Shouts of "Watch out there!" or "Haul, you
lubber!" met Mary's ears as a porter maneuvered her and
her luggage aboard the West African cargo boat, the *Lagos*.

On board, Mary studied the quarters that were to be
home to her for several weeks. The bunk was about five
feet long and two feet wide, small even for her slim figure
and medium height. She lifted a corner of the blanket covering the bunk and gave the thin horsehair mattress a thump.
This was no luxury ship. The *Lagos* was one of a line of
small steamers that went between England and the Coast,
taking manufactured goods to Africa in exchange for oil
from oil palms, ivory, and sometimes rubber. Mary inhaled
the odors of the ship, listening to the sounds outside her
cabin, and felt a rush of affection for the small, grubby
vessel. In her satchel was a clipping of an article that her
cousin had sent her, called "A Week in a Palm Oil Tub."
Tub or not, Mary thought, as she arranged her belongings,
it would do for her.

There was a blast from the steamer's whistle. Mary hurried up on deck to watch a tug haul the ship out to sea. In
the crowd on the dock, she made out the waving hands and
worried faces of those friends who had come to wish her
bon voyage. They looked as somber as if she were going
to the end of the world. She waved back cheerfully, her

spirits rising steadily as the ship moved away from shore. Behind the cargo boat's stern, the water frothed like a white river.

When the people on shore could no longer be seen, Mary went back to her cabin, glancing curiously at her fellow passengers on the way. Some of them, judging by their air and garb and sun-browned faces, were Gold Coasters of the type she had met in the Canaries. She had a whole set of questions in mind to ask them, between now and the day when she would set foot on African soil for the first time. A Gold Coaster was a person who had spent a number of years on that part of Africa's coast now known as Ghana but once called the Gold Coast.

In the days that followed, Mary found the Gold Coasters only too eager to dwell on the dangers from crocodiles or gorillas or the climate of Africa. Two men seemed to vie with each other in telling her hair-raising stories. One, whom she secretly dubbed "Whiskers" because of the luxuriant hair on his chin, was an old Gold Coaster. The other was known as a River Man because his African experience had been on that continent's greatest rivers, the Nile, the Congo, the Bonny and the Ogowé.

Rough weather descended on the ship in the Bay of Biscay but it brought Mary more excitement than alarm. Sitting in the salon, she watched a giant wave make a green-handed slap at the deck with a feeling of exhilaration. But the woman sitting across from her shuddered. "I've never been to sea before and I don't think I ever want to go again."

"This is only my second ocean voyage," Mary said, "but I'm sure we're in no danger." She got up and went out on deck.

The rising wind and the creaking of the vessel seemed determined to make a liar of her. The crew rushed around in oilskins, battening down all loose articles, checking every detail of the wallowing ship. Mary thought of the doctor who had advised her to die where she could ride in a plumed hearse. She was not eager to die, but if she had a choice of places she thought she would prefer to die at sea in this hearse which was plumed with waves and wind.

The whiskered Gold Coaster came to stand beside Mary and some of the others who had joined her. "We could use some ju ju about now, it seems to me."

"What on earth is ju ju?" the woman next to Mary asked. She was the wife of a minor British official in Nigeria, on her first trip to Africa.

Whiskers shrugged. "Religion, I guess you'd have to say. A native charm or god of some kind. Some people call it fetish. Whatever it's called, the natives all practice it, in one form or another." He moved away to speak to someone before Mary could follow up the subject. She was very much interested in the matter of fetish. Her father had discussed the various primitive objects he had brought home with him at times and had explained that a fetish was any object supposed to possess magical powers, as in curing disease or warding off harm. Mary thought of her father's old compass, stowed in her baggage. Bringing it along had made her feel closer to her father's memory; she felt that using the instrument he had so often held in his hands gave her a special sense of direction. In its own way, then, the compass was a charm, a fetish. Superstition had its roots deep in the minds of white races as well as among the darker-skinned humans, she thought.

The *Lagos* staggered through the blasts only to encounter worse storms farther on. When the ship reached the Canary Islands, all the other women disembarked, including the British official's wife, who said she would wait there for her husband to meet her, instead of going on to Nigeria.

Although Mary was the only woman passenger when the ship left the Canaries again, by that time the men on board had accepted her presence despite their fears concerning her stay in Africa. As the ship neared Cape Verde, the hot breath of the tropics came to meet it. The *Lagos* did not touch shore along this stretch of the journey because of the great reef that lay along the Cape.

As the ship traveled southward, the veteran Coasters paid very little more attention to the sultry air, with its threat of storm, than they did to the smoke of their pipes as they sat on deck, baked by sun one minute and drenched by violent showers the next.

Mary gave up all attempts to shelter herself under her umbrella. She could not get her fill of weather and sea, and even when a tornado threatened, she stayed on deck, watching in fascination. The sky was torn by violence, no matter in what direction she looked. At one part of the horizon, columns of black cloud reared up against a pale green background. To leeward, lightning leaped from a cloud as black as tar.

"Here she comes!" a man yelled.

The wind yelped through the rigging, tearing at Mary's hair and billowing her skirts into sails. The first officer stood on top of a pile of awnings to keep them from being blown away. He called to Mary, "This'll give the deck a first class wash."

Captain Murray, who commanded the *Lagos*, passed Mary with a shake of his head. "Sharks'll have you if you go overboard, miss. Better get below decks."

Before he could turn his suggestion into an order, Mary began to shout questions at him. Taken by surprise, the flat-nosed, veteran captain found himself suddenly involved in giving her a short course on meteorology, barometric pressure, and various nautical matters. With a grunt, he broke off. "This is no time for gabbing. You'll get your fill of wet weather before we dock."

The ship's journey to Sierra Leone, the first African country at which the *Lagos* would stop, proved Captain Murray's prediction true. The rain came in one swishing, rushing cataract of water, kicking up such a spray when it hit the sea that it was impossible to see beyond the deck rails.

The ship made its way carefully past Bathurst and Cape St. Mary's. Freetown, the port capital of Sierra Leone, came closer, the *Lagos* feeling her way now between the rocks and shoals. The ship dropped anchor in the harbor outside Freetown in late evening, with the weather still so thick that not even the light on Cape Sierra Leone could be seen. Captain Murray decided not to risk trying to get inside the harbor.

"The air's so heavy I feel as if I could bite it," Mary said to a fellow passenger as they stared over the rail into the gray night.

"Solid malaria," her companion said with a chuckle. "That's what the regulars call this kind of weather. They claim it thickens up on shore and comes out here to meet strangers like you, to warn you off."

The anchored ship rolled all night long and no one slept well. Dawn found Mary and the rest of the passengers on deck. A breeze came up and lifted the mist, rolling it upward over the land, portions of it clinging to the forests of the mountains in the distance.

Mary felt a thrill of joy at the sight of Freetown Harbor. The book on pirates that she had read so often as a girl had described every bay and mountain, including the famous Pirate's Bay. The wooded hills of the Cape rose behind the bays to become parts of the mountain called Sierra Leone. The city of Freetown was a feast of color. Most of the houses were wood with corrugated iron roofs, but a few buildings were of red stone. An occasional thatched roof festooned with creepers was visible.

After the ship docked and Mary was on shore she walked through the streets. Flowering plants made fragrant jungles of house yards. Frangipani, orange flowers, magnolias, oleanders and flowers she had never before seen and did not know the names of, were visible everywhere. On the side streets paved with springy Bahama grass, barefooted men and women walked lightly, carrying enormous bundles of produce or lumber or palm oil.

Making her way through the noisy crowds of people, pigs, goats, sheep and dogs, Mary felt glad that Freetown was not her destination. It was only a gateway to the real Africa she wanted to know.

The steamer's whistle sounded a warning call, its blast rising above the raucous cries of crows staring down at her from the top of the Christian cathedral. Mary followed the other passengers back to the *Lagos*.

Late afternoon found the cargo ship once more engulfed in misty, wet weather. Mary, writing in her cabin, felt moisture seeping into her bones. She wiped a hand across the cabin wall and her palm came away thoroughly wet. A scorpion dropped from somewhere, landing on the floor beside her bunk. Mary watched him, wondering if he had more dangerous relatives in the river countries she was headed for.

In the salon, later, she found the male passengers deep in a discussion of driver, or soldier, ants which came in hordes and devoured everything in their path. She listened, wondering if their tales of horror could possibly be true. A sharp tingle raced along her spine. Was she really as brave as she thought?

As the *Lagos* weathered the shoals of St. Anna and came finally into the port of Monrovia, Liberia, Captain Murray pointed out what appeared to be a series of beautiful lakes threading into each other, between the sand beach and the forest wall.

"They're pretty now," he said, "but when it's dry those lakes are pure mud."

It was to Liberia, Mary remembered, that the United States, in 1820, had tried to return some descendants of the Africans they had bought as slaves. Well-meant as it had been, the effort was a tragic error. Second and third generation Negroes no longer possessed the native resistance to malaria, and many of them died. The project was abandoned when it was realized that returning slaves to Africa was not the answer to the problem of slavery.

The coast along Liberia was the famous Grain Coast, so known because of the "grains of paradise" which in earlier times had been its chief export. The Grain Coast was the home of the Kru tribes. Krumen were Negroes who had never been enslaved nor traded in slaves themselves, a fact of which they were very proud. Basketwork tattoo extending from forehead to the tip of a Kruman's nose was the mark that told the world of this honorable record—for it was not only white men who dealt in slaves; African natives sold other Africans during the slave trade days.

On deck, Mary tasted the grains of paradise a little too boldly. She bit into one of the capsules, seeds of the meleguetta pepper, and then wildly fanned her mouth. "Quick— some water!" she gasped to the Kruboy who had grinningly satisfied her curiosity about the seeds. It was like biting red hot pepper.

A chuckling Coaster thrust a dipper of water into Mary's hand from the ship's supply. "Not much trade in this stuff now. The idea went around for a while that these meleguetta grains were poisonous, but they're not. The Krus claim the stuff makes a good healing plaster."

Still choking from the fire in her throat, Mary managed to sputter, "I wish you'd imparted that information sooner. I'd have tried the seeds on the outside instead of the inside of me." A number of Krus had boarded the ship when it dropped anchor and now they were carrying on such a chatter and clamor she could hardly make herself heard. "Are Africans always this noisy?"

"Or noisier. All their business is carried on with their tongues and lungs, since Africa has no written language."

"I know." Mary remembered her father's feeling of frustration over this.

The Coaster continued, "When a native's not talking to his neighbor, he talks to ghosts. Most Africans believe that their dead relatives come back to act as guardians for their welfare. I saw a man once, in the middle of a palaver—an argument we'd call it, miss—turn and say to the empty air, 'That's the truth, isn't it, Mother?' His mother had been dead for years but I almost believed she was there, myself, the way he spoke."

"He was lucky to have such a belief," Mary murmured, a wistful envy touching her. There had been moments during this voyage when she had all but spoken aloud to her mother's and father's ghosts, but belief in their reality was not as strong with her as with the Kru, unfortunately. Still, watching them, she felt an increasing sense of kinship with them and the other Africans, in spite of the differences between her way of life and theirs.

A sudden uproar caused Mary to turn around. A tattooed

Kruman, a brilliant draping of cloth around his torso and legs, was waving angry fists at Captain Murray.

The man with Mary said, "The captain's hiring some Krumen to come along with the ship. He's offering cash but they want goods—gunpowder, mostly, and liquor."

The Kruman doing the arguing appeared to be a chief. In trade English, he said, "What good him money, Cappy? Suppose you gib tobacco, gun—he be fit for trade, but money—" The chief spat disgustedly.

Captain Murray gave in, agreeing to make payment in cloth, guns, knives and similar articles. Every object used in trade had an accepted value or price, and could be totaled to an equivalent of a cash wage.

Mary watched and listened as she had used to watch and listen to her father and his friends discussing science. Who knew, perhaps she would find a knowledge of trade and trade terms very useful when she reached that part of Africa where most of her research would be done! Her plan was to stop at various places along the lower West Coast to seek for desirable specimens of fishes and insects—and to seek also whatever Africa might offer her heart and soul.

🌿 CHAPTER FIVE

AS THE STEAMER MADE ITS WAY ALONG THE SOUTHERN EDGE of the great western hump of Africa, Mary had increasing glimpses of the giant mangrove swamps extending inland from the coast along the banks of rivers that emptied into the sea. From the coast city of Lagos, Nigeria, onward, the swamps grew steadily thicker. The walls of mangroves, with occasional aerial roots reaching toward the sky, seemed sinister, green-black traps waiting to catch the unwary.

When the wind was right, Mary was forced to breathe in the stench of the swamps. Mosquitoes and mangrove flies must be happily hatching there, she thought, across the miles of water. She was growing impatient to try her skill at scientific collecting but she would not have a chance until the *Lagos* turned and made its way inland, up one of the rivers. In the meantime, she continued to pick up phrases of trade English, a half-native, half-English language. She watched the Krumen who had joined the ship at Sierra Leone, some as passengers wanting to go farther south along the coast, some as additional crew.

One evening, music came drifting up to the ship's salon where Mary and other passengers were sitting after their evening meal. It was a strange music, exquisitely clear and sweet, and it came from the lower deck. Mary left her chair to go out on deck in the hope of finding out what instrument might be making the unfamiliar music.

48

From the stairway between the decks she saw a dark-skinned Kruman beating on a sort of xylophone with a tiny hammer. She remembered having read about West African marimbas; this was probably an example.

"Now what are you up to?" a voice growled in her ear. She turned to see Captain Murray. "I was just taking a music lesson," she said meekly. Less meekly she boasted, "I'll wager I could play that instrument of his myself."

The captain squinted at her, grunted, and then said abruptly, "Come along." He guided her down the iron steps and in among the startled natives, explaining to the marimba player that the "ma" wanted to try the instrument once.

There were wide grins on the dark faces as the marimba player relinquished his hammer to Mary.

She braced her shoulders and lifted her chin, aware that the usually talkative Kru were very silent. Her mother had taught her to play the small, reed organ at Southgate but that was different. This primitive instrument was simply a set of hollow gourds covered by strips of hard wood and fastened within a reed frame. Intensely aware of the watching Krumen, she grew stiff with stage fright and could not think what to play.

"Try 'The Last Rose,'" Captain Murray said, trying to be helpful.

It was not very appropriate, Mary thought, but the only other tune she could think of was "Rule, Brittania," and that was even less so. She struck a few practice blows. Encouraged, she finally managed to play several phrases of "The Last Rose of Summer."

Stopping, she looked out at her audience. They were still grinning but now they began to slap their thighs and stamp their feet in what, she hoped, was approval. The marimba player tried out his English. "Berry fine ting, ma. All same for one, you play plenty plenty fine."

Mary's own rare smile flashed in answer as she handed his mallet back to him. Filled with satisfaction and triumph, she felt that she was reaching across the gulf that separated her race from the races of Africa and establishing some sort of communication, at least briefly. Emboldened, she tried out her own trade English on the musician, asking about the way the instrument had been made. She pointed at the little holes on the side of each gourd, curious about the thin membrane stretched over these holes.

"Him come from skin," she was told.

Mary swallowed. Her shock showed in her face and then she heard Captain Murray chuckle.

"The skin of a big spider, Miss Kingsley."

Relieved at the explanation, Mary stayed long enough to watch the Krumen drag out other instruments, one of which was a long drum. This was covered with goatskin and the player beat it fiercely, making Mary's ears ache. Other instruments were taken up and Mary watched the men's hands manipulating the various sticks and hammers, thinking about the spiderskin covering. What a delicate skill, to be able to use anything so fragile. She hoped that her own skill would be as successful when it came to preserving the insects she hoped to find for her collection.

It was still August when the *Lagos* anchored at Old Calabar, an English-administered settlement in Nigeria. It was also still the rainy season and the downpour drummed on the roof of Government House, Sir Claude Macdonald's quarters. Sir Claude was England's Commissioner for the oil rivers, those rivers which were the routes for bringing kegs of palm oil to the western African coast from the interior villages. Captain Murray had brought Mary to the Commissioner to find out about collecting fishes on the Bonny, one of the oil rivers under his commissionership.

"I told her the Bonny would be especially stinking just now," the captain told Sir Claude, "but she's determined, so we'll take her upriver with us on our regular trip for oil, if you've no objection."

"No, indeed," Sir Claude said. "It's a great pleasure to meet someone with such spirit." He had arisen to be introduced to Mary and now he drew a chair across the verandah toward her. "It's a pity that Lady Macdonald's in England. I imagine you're missing white women's company. Are you boiling your water and taking quinine?"

Mary assured him that she was. With a glance at Captain Murray, she said, "I'm getting to be an old Coaster fast, under the captain's training."

"She was born a Coaster, if you ask me," Captain Murray said, looking at Mary with approval.

Mary began to question the commissioner about the settlement, the swamps, the wild life, the natives. She tucked each answer away in her mental filing cabinet until she had time to note them in her traveling journal. Sir Claude was warm and considerate, pleasantly different from some of the colonial administrators she had met. Some of them, although they were honorable and even sensitive men, seemed unable or unwilling to see beyond the color of an African's skin to the human being like themselves beneath.

"We'd better get back to the ship, ma'am," Captain Murray interrupted finally. "The ship's crying for palm oil, like she always does once we get to the rivers."

Mary unfurled her umbrella against the downpour as they started back. It was almost useless against the tropical torrents but it had already become both companion and staff to her. In moments of doubt or melancholy—even her delight in Africa could not keep melancholy away when she was off guard—the umbrella was something to cling to or lean on or, if need came, to use as a weapon. And it was a scrap of England.

Captain Murray paused a moment to speak to Sir Claude. Mary went on alone, holding the umbrella firmly against the rain. Natives at their chores paused, watching her, chattering in a tongue she could not understand. Here on the coast, most of them had seen many white women but there was a look of curiosity on their faces when they saw the slim figure in dark skirts holding an absurd umbrella over her like a strange, black flower. A few of the faces also had a sullen look.

If I could only get to know them better, she thought. If I could only take some knowledge of value back with me to England that would help all of us humans to improve our relationships with one another.

Fish, she reminded herself sternly. Fish were her job right now.

Mary's enthusiasm for fishing in African rivers dimmed some when Captain Murray turned the *Lagos'* prow riverward and the ship made its way between the banks of the Bonny River. Behind them the river bar stretched in a ridge of white foam. Ahead, brackish water from the tide swirled and sucked at the grotesque trunks of the mangroves, some of which were as thick as the legs of elephants.

Mary wrinkled her nose against the river's smell. "Are you sure you're in the right place, Captain?" she asked with a wry smile.

Captain Murray, despite his own earlier remarks about the Bonny, looked hurt. "It's a nice river when you get used to it," he said.

The jungle landscape slid slowly by. Could a person ever get used to such gloom and smell, to the rain that descended with such a roar that any other sound, even the screech of the winch, was welcome? Mary touched her clothes, certain that mildew must already be coating the cloth from the hundred per cent water content of the air. The melancholy cry of birds made her try to see ashore, in the occasional lessening of the rain's volume.

"Those are curlews," the captain told her. "A pretty sound, once it's known to you." He gave her a sidewise glance as if thinking that the bold-talking Miss Kingsley was neither so bold nor so eager now that Africa had confronted her with this dark and evil-smelling malarial mud.

Mary took her handkerchief from her nostrils and straightened her back. She was not going to let the captain think she was a timid, cringing female he would have to look out for until he could get her on board another ship sailing back to England.

The first stop for the *Lagos* on the Bonny River was a trading post, called a factory. After the walls of mangroves, the white-painted factory and the big palm oil storehouses, all raised on piles above the mud, seemed almost beautiful in spite of the continuing stench. Native canoes were moored against the mud shore, rocking listlessly in the thick water, some of the canoes containing rotting fish.

As the ship anchored, the captain said, "Here's your chance to palaver for a canoe and crew to take you after those precious fish of yours, miss." He studied her. "Unless you've changed your mind."

Mary gripped her umbrella. "And why would I ever do that, Captain Murray?"

He smiled. "I thought you might have got scared out there on the river. I see that I was wrong."

Mary picked her way past the canoes and mud and rotting fish heads, toward the shore, trying not to show how hard it was to breathe the air. A small, naked child came running around the edge of the oil storehouse. His leg was swollen with some infection and there was a look of fever in his dark eyes. Mary thought of the drugs in her medicine kit, of her nursing training—but before any of the thoughts became action, the boy's mother darted forward. She picked the boy up and ran off with a backward look of distrust at the strange white woman.

Mary sighed. It would take more than good will on her part to help even where help was needed in Africa.

The next day, as a result of her negotiations with a local chief, Mary found herself in the middle of a canoe, setting forth on her first real search for rare fish. The canoe, made from a hollowed-out log, made the grubby *Lagos* seem like a floating palace. Two natives made up her crew and although they were stalwart-looking, she felt considerable trepidation over going out to brave the sidestreams of the Bonny with only natives and her own resolution to depend on. In one hand she clutched Dr. Henry Günther's book, *Study of Fishes*. A protective arm was stretched over her equipment: a round net, three strong fish lines, and a few of her bottles for preserving the fish. At her feet was a can of evil-smelling bait and a broken calabash shell for bailing out water. A supply of manioc, the "bread" of Africa, completed the cargo except for the dirty water thrown on board by the men's paddles. The manioc, a gummy substance like unrefined tapioca, was made from a native root that Mary secretly thought should never have been dug from the ground.

When they reached a creek which had been recommended to Mary as the best place for fish, she set to work with her net and line. The natives, too, each threw out a line. It was very quiet in the swampy shadows, the only sounds being the slaps of the two Negroes when insects landed on them, and the occasional rasping cry of the gray parrots flying overhead.

With a gasp of triumph, Mary brought two shimmering, bright-colored fish up in her net. Drying her fingers on a rag, she checked through Günther's book to try to identify them. There was no description of the gasping creatures. With a hope that the fish were a rare species, she placed them in her collecting sack. Later, she would preserve them in alcohol.

Suddenly, at her back, there was a loud, startling grunt. Mary turned, her pole jerking. A giant catfish thrashed about in the bottom of the canoe, fighting against a fish-hook, its fins and horns threatening the bare feet and legs of the natives. The men hopped about wildly to avoid the fish, one of them meantime trying to kill the three-foot, yellow-gray monster with a club.

"Lef em, lef em!" Mary shouted. "Heave em water one time!" As the ugly, fleshy whiskers of the fish grazed her skirts she backed away. The canoe lurched and water slopped over the stern.

Her trade English failed her and she cried out, "Careful! We'll capsize!" As the canoe jarred against a bank, Mary tossed Günther's book onto a comparatively dry spot. If she didn't drown, she would need that book.

The native in the far end of the canoe lifted his paddle and lunged toward the catfish. The man ahead of him moved at the same time and the paddle crashed against him instead of the fish. The canoe shuddered, rocked, and went over, the howls of the two men ringing in Mary's ears as she plunged to the bottom of the creek.

She sputtered against the rank water and fought her way to an upright position, trying not to swallow. Captain Murray had told her that eight of the eleven men posted at the factory had died in the last yellow fever epidemic. Plastered with mud, her skirt floating about her, Mary half swam, half waded as she looked around for the equipment that had been tossed out of the boat with her. The canoe floated nearby, bottom upward. Beside it floated the tin can, the calabash, and the paddles. The sour manioc, she hoped, had gone down and would stay there.

One of the men had managed to climb onto the bank and was busily hauling out his friend by the legs, the latter having got entangled in a fish net caught in the river mud. Both men appeared to have forgotten their employer.

Mary shouted at them, making her way to the canoe as best she could. She tried to get the vessel upright, meantime.

Finally the men came splashing toward her, one of them saying, "Canoe bery slippery one time, ma."

Among the three of them, they got the canoe righted. The men retrieved the floating articles and started to climb back into the canoe with Mary but she pointed at Dr. Günther's book on the river bank.

"Book bery big ju ju, my country," she explained.

As the native came wading back with the precious book, holding it safely above the water, she heard a strange whine and a sighing cough. She looked beyond the African at the bank he had just left. A narrow snout was thrusting itself up out of the water not five yards away!

She cried out and pointed, just as the man with the book climbed into the canoe.

One look at the evil-faced crocodile was all her men

needed. They began to ply their paddles so swiftly that the brown water churned. Clinging to the canoe's side, Mary looked at her dripping clothes and at the forlornly small shape of the two specimen fish in the sack. Her first venture at collecting could scarcely be called a triumph, but it was a beginning.

🌿 CHAPTER SIX

MARY WAS ON THE DECK OF THE *Lagos*, AS USUAL, WHEN IT anchored in the harbor of Loanda in the Portuguese province of Angola, West Africa. After the long ocean voyage and the side trips up the oil rivers and back again to the ocean, the *Lagos* had become home to her, but now she was going to have to leave it and its friendly crew and find other means of getting where she wanted to go.

Captain Murray, when he had brought his ship around and preparations were under way for landing the passengers, came to say good-by to his favorite among them, Mary.

"Now don't you go taking chances on those rivers for the sake of a few fish," he said. He fiddled with the braid on his cap a minute or two and added gruffly, "I'm hoping to have you sail back with us, next trip around, so see that you stay alive."

Genuinely moved, Mary turned to look into the captain's kind face. "I take a lot of killing," she said gently. "By all the rules, I should have been done for years ago but there's a streak of toughness in me that won't let go."

He smiled. "Right, then; I'll say so long until the next time." He touched his cap and left her.

Two other ship's officers came by to take a personal leave of Mary. One of them was the ship's second mate, who had spent much time teaching Mary "trade" or "Kru" English. He said, "I wish you'd go home, miss. Africa's no place for a nice lady like you and if you've good sense, as I know you have, you'll turn around right now and head back to England."

"And waste all that language you taught me?" Mary shook her head.

Although she shared none of the fears for herself that her traveling companions had expressed, it was with some sadness that Mary watched the *Lagos* pull out of the harbor, a day later, leaving her behind. She felt more alone than she had at any time on the journey. She had become attached to her "palm oil tub" and the men who operated her.

When the *Lagos* was out of sight, she turned away to go and examine the beautiful Loanda native canoes with their sand-colored sails of matting and their graceful lines. Finding an Angola fisherman who spoke trade English, she began to ask about ways of getting upriver to fish.

The Portuguese officials in the coast towns of Angola were very pleasant to Mary and she enjoyed her stay in their territory. It was also scientifically rewarding because she obtained a variety of fish, most of them by means of a stockade trap. This was a trap built by driving stakes close together in the river, leaving open the upriver end. The water coming downstream would wash fish into the stockade. When it was full, the opening was closed, and the fishermen took the fish out of the trap and put them in baskets. From these baskets, Mary was allowed to choose the specimens she wished to keep.

At night she worked at bottling and labeling her finds, listening, as she worked, to the song of the African darkness —a chorus composed of insects, monkeys, occasional birds, and small, wild creatures she could not identify. Sometimes, when there was a moon, she fished at night. That was how she discovered a species of "singing" fish. It was a fresh water fish called the *ning ning* by the natives because of the noise it made.

Another fish serenader was the saltwater drum fish. In Loanda Harbor one moonlit night she watched these drum fish move in a wreath around the canoe where she sat, their noses bum-bumming against the side of the canoe in a kind of rhythm.

One of Mary's keenest pleasures was to watch the fish in their own water world. If she kept quiet, the fish went on with their ordinary activities of hunting, feeding, playing and fighting. Holding a handful of crumbs under the water for the little warrior fish to nibble, Mary experienced a delight she could not have explained to anyone.

The insect life in Africa provided no such satisfactions, but it did provide adventure. Seventy-five per cent of African insects sting, she learned; five per cent bite, and the rest make their homes in human flesh. On a journey from St. Paul de Loanda up to Gaboon, she stopped at an African village near the port of Kabinda. She was walking down the dusty street when an African family poured out from one of the huts, screaming and crying. They were followed by whatever else lived in the hut, including some rats and a scorpion or two.

Apprehensive, Mary stopped where she was. The mother and father, after looking frenziedly around at their children and the possessions they had carried out with them, suddenly began to scream even louder.

"Whatever is wrong?" Mary asked her guide.

"Dey say all time ants all over dey house, ma." As other families began rushing from other houses, he added, "Much ants many places, mebbe," looking fearfully down at the ground below his own bare feet.

Driver ants! Mary shuddered. Those hordes could strip a living creature to the bone. She went toward the terrified family to try to calm them, but the woman kept gesturing wildly, pointing to the house, and twisting her hands.

"Is there someone still inside?" Mary asked, indicating to the guide that he was to interpret her question.

Wild nodding of the woman's head.

"A baby?" Mary asked. Anyone who could walk would have come out with the others, she felt.

Another vigorous nod.

Mary hesitated. But it was obvious that neither the father nor mother could get up the courage to go back after the baby. Grimly, she gathered her long skirts about her so they would not brush the ground. "Where him be?"

"In him far corner for floor!" her guide said.

Mary charged into the hut. There in the far corner lay a bundle swarming with the vicious ants. She snatched the bundle up, holding it at arm's length to try to dodge the crawling river of drivers, and rushed out. She thrust the bundle at the delighted parents and ran on by to plunge her arms into the nearest water barrel. Water was the only weapon against the terrible ants.

She looked up, her arms dripping, to see the native father bringing the bundle she had rescued to the same water barrel. Horrified, she watched him douse the bundle in the water, immersing it as he shouted for joy.

Not until the bundle was brought up out of the barrel again, minus its coverings and also minus the driver ants, did Mary discover the kind of "child" she had rescued. The bundle contained a ham.

During her months in Africa, Mary came across the

driver ants more than once. The pouring torrents of the rainy season had their uses as a shower to wash away the dangerous pests.

Mary made no attempt to add driver ants to her collection. She did send back to England an ant's nest, but not that of a driver ant. The nest was the size of an apple and was stuck together with a spidery web.

In spite of the friendliness of the Portuguese, Mary was amazed at their handling of colonial affairs; they were even less efficient and informed than her own country about their African colony. The home government in Portugal had ordered street lighting and a water system for Loanda in a sudden burst of colonial concern. Until then, the water for the city had been brought by boat from the Bengo River. There had been no street lamps at all, except native bush torches.

When the street lamps arrived, they turned out to be gas lamps—and there was no gas in Loanda. Oil lamps were then ordered, but the lamplighters had no ladders and so had to scale the post as best they could, each evening, to light the city. Sometimes dawn was showing before the lamps were all lit.

The water system was all right except that native women were not accustomed to paying a fee for water, and they did their best to avoid it. The Angola women, when they gathered at the central hydrant or standpipe, made an arrangement whereby one of their number would scratch the official in charge of the pipe, distracting his attention, while the others drew water both for themselves and her.

From Loanda Mary went north, by land, to another seacoast town, Ambriz, and from there on up to Kabinda. She took a steamer up the Congo River for some distance and made short trips, alone, to visit native tribes. Every hour she spent on the rivers or with the primitive peoples made her feel more and more certain that Africa, especially its South West Coast, was her destiny.

The journey was an almost continual adventure. Upset canoes, crocodiles and escapades among the villagers became routine features of the life she had chosen. But she was beginning really to know Africa—its incredible beauty, its fearsome climate, its disease and its fever swamps. When she felt discouraged or tired, some majestic forest tree or river scene would boost her spirits. When she came back out of the rivers and the bush, a meeting with an interesting native or trader could make her forget all hardships in the stimulation of their conversations.

She made her way up rivers and creeks without the help of white men, having been advised by Captain Murray of the *Lagos* how to be her own captain and navigator and how to hire her own crews to man the rude river boats. No native ever attempted to do her any real harm and many opened their homes and their hearts to this strange "ma," whose like they had never seen before.

On long trips she traveled by whatever coastal vessel was available, and in this way saw something of the Belgian Congo and the German territory of the Cameroons. In the Cameroons, she had her first glimpse of the great mountain peak Mungo Mah Lobeh. Rising almost fourteen thousand feet into chill air, the peak was sometimes wreathed in black tornado clouds, but sometimes it glinted with gold and green and rose. Mary gazed at it in awe. In spite of her dread of the snow and cold on its crest, and her fear of heights, she felt an urge to climb the peak. But there was not time. She had allowed herself only six months for this first look at Africa and she needed that time for those other, more urgent goals of study and collecting. She would come back again, she promised herself, and then perhaps she would challenge the great peak.

In the bush, where so much of Mary's time was spent, there were plenty of challenges of a different kind. She was carrying a small revolver in her bag but she hoped never to have to use it against either beast or man. The cough of a leopard or the bray of zebras would bring her to a halt, but only to try to catch a glimpse of the wild creatures without risking an attack. There were no lions and no trumpeting elephants or plodding rhinoceroses in this part of Africa, but there were gazelles that leaped like light among the woodland trails of the coast. There were also elands, and serpents, and a million crawling insects.

The king of this African forest was the gorilla. Often, Mary heard the gorilla's bark or thunder-voiced roar and once, in the company of half-naked hunters, streaked with red clay and bristling with knives and arrows, she had glimpsed a giant gorilla lumbering through the jungle. He had looked too human for her to feel comfortable when the hunters finally brought him down.

Mary loved the great forest from the first moment she saw it and once wrote that nothing in life was as fascinating as spending a night out in it. "It is like being shut up in a library whose books you cannot read . . . if you do fall under its spell, it takes all the color out of other kinds of living."

The African native presented for the white man, she felt, a mind-forest similar in its mystery and potentiality. Until a person had lived with the great trees or studied at close hand the native mind, it was impossible to see what was worth seeing in either of them.

Mary spent as little time as possible in the Belgian Congo,

where a ruthless policy of exploitation left results that withered her morale and brought on an attack of acute melancholy. The hands of some native rubber workers, including children, had been lopped off at the wrist when the quota of rubber was not brought in on schedule. The natives of the region lived in poverty and fear while the Belgian army officers in charge carried out their king's orders.

The French Congo was a different matter and it was there that she met a very unusual trader, a man named R. J. Dennett. Dennett took time from his factory management concerns to give Mary many valuable details about the local tribes. He was an authority on the distribution of such diseases as sleeping sickness and had written a valuable book about the Fjorts, one of the African tribes.

Making her own notes, Mary wondered if they would ever add up to a book. She was no writer but there was so much to be said for and about Africa that she thought she would sometime like to try putting her thoughts and knowledge into book form. She felt both gratitude and admiration for the traders. They were lonely men, mostly, and they welcomed her company in their outposts. Drunk or sober, sick or well, they shared what they had with her, and Dennett seemed to her the most remarkable of these men. She was sitting with him once in a very lonely hut-factory, the room illuminated only by a wick floating in oil, when he broke off their conversation to say very somberly, "Now let us have a little talk with God." Mary was startled, for there had not been any discussion of religion in their conversation, but she saw his face in the light from the wick floating in oil beside him on the table and realized that he was completely sincere.

Later, wandering up and down the continent with her fish net in one hand and her umbrella usually in the other, Mary often thought of that evening with Dennett. In Africa, even for a rough trader, it was easy to feel that one could pause and look and listen and "talk with God," because His brooding presence seemed very near.

On the practical side, Mary's knowledge of trade was increasing rapidly. She went among the primitive tribes as an accepted dealer in the trinkets, tobacco, hardware and cloth that the Africans coveted. These items in her luggage opened more doors to her than any armed escort or government passport could have done. As a trader she sat, an honored guest, at remote inland camp fires. She gained the confidence of the old, wrinkled women who often held great power in their tribes, by understanding the trading worth of her merchandise. Even the witch doctors learned to trust her and shared a few of their secrets with her.

Once, when she was living temporarily in a deserted house that had been occupied some years before by the famous explorer and newspaper man, H. M. Stanley, someone tapped on the shutters at eleven o'clock at night.

Mary called out, "Wait one time," and got up, slipping into her clothing again. It was probably some native wanting tobacco, she thought tiredly, and she was going to give him a good tongue lashing for disturbing her at such an hour.

When she opened the door, she found one of her witch doctor friends standing there. He asked, "You be big man, suppose pusson sick?"

Whether she was a big man or not Mary's humility would not let her say, but the "pusson" must be very sick indeed for a native doctor to come to her for help.

The doctor went on, "Pusson sick too much, pusson live for die. You fit for come?"

Mary hesitated. The jungle night beyond her visitor's shoulder seemed to be several shades darker than his skin.

Still, if someone was sick and needed her help . . . It might even be one of the Portuguese officials who had helped her get around when she first came. Why had she studied medicine if not to help when she was called on?

"I'm fit," she told the witch doctor.

She was about to follow him when he asked one more question. "No fit to talk?" he asked anxiously.

He did not want her to tell anyone that she had been on this mission. She couldn't blame him. His reputation was at stake. This time she answered promptly, "No fit." She had no desire to boast of any midnight errands of mercy to anyone.

Fortunately, the witch doctor was dressed in white, or Mary would have lost him as soon as they were inside the forest, because of the intense darkness of the night. He led her up over a low hill and then down into even deeper woods. Thoughts of leopards and gorillas and various vicious insects swarmed into Mary's mind, but she dared not look around her for fear of losing the white gleam that was her guide's clothing. A sleeping python had draped itself over a branch that hung across the path, and in the darkness her guide did not recognize his ancient enemy—at least not until he had walked right against it. When he realized what it was he ducked under the living festoon and began to run, yelling something to Mary. She followed him as fast as she could, almost as terrified of losing sight of her guide as she was of the aroused snake which she could hear crashing off into the bush behind them.

When they had reached a village they found the sick man on the ground in front of one of the huts. Mary, who always carried medical supplies in her handbag, saw that the patient was suffering from a bad case of fever. She gave the witch doctor the proper dose of quinine for the patient and let

him administer it, observing a respectful silence while he
chanted an incantation and added some herbs of his own
to the dose before giving it to the sick man. Together, she
and the witch doctor waited until the medicine took effect
and the sick man began to improve. Early in the morning,
the grateful witch doctor escorted Mary back to her house,
accepting her invitation to come inside for a cup of tea with
her. They talked for an hour, to Mary's delight, about his
profession, life, and philosophy. What the witch doctor
said, according to Mary's later account of it, sounded like
an excerpt from one of Wolfgang von Goethe's books. She
told the doctor that he must have got his philosophy from
some white man, but he said firmly and with dignity, "That
no be white man fash, that be country fash. White man no
fit to savee our fash."

Maybe he was right, Mary thought when her visitor had
gone. Maybe the white man was not able to understand the
African's philosophy, at least not yet. The white man, too,
needed educating. "We will all have to educate each other,"
she told herself as she once more prepared for bed.

Permission to venture into the wilder parts of the various
territories had to be secured from whatever colonial power,
British or German or French, was in control of it. Most of
the officials Mary dealt with were co-operative, if worried,
and she ignored their expressions of horror over her plans.
Away from the government centers, she depended, at least
at first, on the white missionaries—Presbyterians, Catholics
and Methodists—who had come out ahead of her to this unknown world. She disapproved of the ideas most of them
had about the African but did approve of the work they did
in educating the children and fighting disease. Among the
missionaries were a few who won more than her approval;

they had her admiration and respect. One of these was Dr. John Nassau, the Presbyterian missionary who had founded the American mission station at Lambaréné in 1851, in French Equatorial Africa. When the French later took over the mission, Dr. Nassau moved to Libreville where Mary met him not long after she arrived in that part of Africa. He was of immense help to her in the anthropological side of her mission, because he had studied the native religions so thoroughly during his years there.

The few fears Mary had had when she first set foot on the African continent were fast disappearing. When she was in mangrove territory, she loved to paddle alone among the trees at high tide, not always remembering to get back to the main stream of the river before the tide went out again and left her almost stranded on the mud.

Even when she did remember to start back in time, there was the ever-present crocodile to worry about, and the mangrove flies to fight. Once, one of the crocodiles caught her in shallow enough water so that he was able to get his clawed front feet over the stern of her canoe. She retreated to the bow to keep the canoe in balance, and hit him on the nose with her paddle until he let go. She later made fun of her own courage on this occasion by saying that it would be an understatement to say she was not frightened.

On another occasion, when she was in a lagoon with a native crew on a moonlight night, she kept hearing the peculiar whine and sighing cough of crocodiles even in her sleep. At last she woke up enough to see that one of the sleeping men in her crew was dangling his leg over the side of the canoe. Again she used her paddle, this time to wake the man up, for which he was particularly grateful because, he said, he had lost a valuable uncle in this same swamp, right out of a canoe, to a crocodile. "Uncle now devil-ghost. He be out dere, mebbe." He gestured toward the shore where the crocodiles generally rested. The Africans believed that a relative could go bad after death and come back in the body of a crocodile or snake or other such enemies of man. Mary assured him that she and her paddle would do their best to keep off his ghost uncle or any other crocodile which hungered for his leg.

All through her trip to Africa, Mary constantly trained herself for physical survival so that she could come back again on a longer excursion. She learned to eat pawpaw, stewed crocodile, insects, boa constrictor and, when she had to, the manioc she detested. She made friends with every class of native: men naked except for a loin cloth or decked in silk robes and shining crowns; women wearing only a scrap of cloth or draped in such volumes of material that they looked like cocoons.

She met all kinds of whites, good and bad, rough and gentle. But nowhere had she been seriously threatened by any person, black or white, when the six months drew to a close. Instead, she thought as she boarded the ship to return to England, she had made many friends in Africa. Watching the coast recede, she felt she was in love, not with a human being, but with a continent. Tired though she was, and often sick, there was a radiance in her face that had not been there when she went out to Africa the August before.

Back among the English mists and the neat yards, the familiar calls of the cuckoo and the domestic sounds of cartwheels and tinkling cups of tea, Mary wrote, "The charm of West Africa is a painful one: it gives you pleasure when you are out there, but when you are back here it gives you pain by calling you. It sends up before your eyes a vision of a wall of dancing white, rainbow-gemmed surf playing on a shore of yellow sand before an audience of stately coco palms; or of a great mangrove-watered bronze river . . . you hear the sweet, long, mellow whistle of the plantain warblers . . . and you want to go back to the coast that is calling you, saying, 'Come back, come back, this is your home.' "

She knew she would go back. And soon.

❧ CHAPTER SEVEN

MOONLIGHT SHIMMERING ON THE OGOWÉ RIVER TURNED THE normally yellow water into an expanse of silvered blackness. Along the banks of the river the great forest stretched its black wall below a purple sky studded with stars. Forest and river was silent now except for the sound of the *Mové*'s screw, an occasional mutter from African passengers sleeping on the lower deck, and the thin cry of the bats when the little river trade steamer veered near shore.

Mary had been home in England the better part of a year and from January to May of this year, 1895, she had stayed at Calabar with Sir Claude and Lady Macdonald. Now here she was, on the great equatorial river she had dreamed of all the time she was in England.

From the upper deck of the *Mové*, she had watched the sun go down and the moon come up. "The day closed with a magnificent, dramatic beauty," she was to write in her journal later. "Dead ahead of us, up through a bank of dun-colored mist rose the moon, a great orb of crimson, spreading down the oil-like, still river, a streak of blood-red reflection. Right astern, the sun sank down into the mist, sent up flushes of amethyst, gold, carmine, and serpent green, before he left the moon in undisputed possession of the black-purple sky."

How often she had dreamed of such scenery while she was away! She had felt obliged to stay with her brother as

72

long as he was at home but her heart yearned for the tropics. When he had gone away again, she had lost no time in planning her own departure. As she faced the white moonlight and black shadows, she thought, Africa is my home.

She was now an official collector for the British Museum, and had been given equipment for her collecting work, which left her more of her own funds for the hiring of canoes and crew to take her on trips farther into the wilderness.

"Must you take these risks, Mary?" Lady Macdonald had asked her when she took leave of the Macdonalds at Calabar.

"Without risk, I'll get nowhere," Mary had replied. She thought of Mary Slessor, the missionary at Okyon with whom she had spent a few days while she was in Calabar.

Miss Slessor, like Dr. Nassau, was one of the missionaries who had won Mary's profound respect. She had lived for eighteen years among the natives of that district, six of those years entirely apart from white people, in a clearing in the forest. She had learned the native languages in order to devote herself with better understanding to fighting the particular native customs and beliefs which were doing the most harm to the native himself.

Among the worst of the superstitions was that twin babies were sent by a devil and must be promptly killed. While Mary was visiting Miss Slessor, the first pair of twins in that immediate district was born. A soon as the news was known, the mother's clothes were torn, she was driven out of her home and finally out of the village, and most of her belongings were thrown out. The infant twins were packed into a box which she carried on her head, and on top of the babies were the only two possesssions she had left: a large brass skillet and two calabashes. Not knowing where else to go, she headed for the missionary's house in the forest with her load. Miss Slessor, told of the news, went barefooted and bareheaded in her haste to meet the unfortunate woman. On her return, she told Mary, "I met the procession four miles from here. You cannot imagine the noise. The whole village was running after her, howling and yowling, telling her to go as far as she could go, before she touched any of them and brought a curse on the whole town."

Miss Slessor carried the box with the twin babies through the broiling sun back to her own house, not even using the regular path because she knew that once the twins had gone along that path no villager would ever again dare to use it. To cut a new path would be a great deal of trouble for them, so she had persuaded the villagers merely to beat a rough trail for her and the unhappy mother.

"Where twins have been, nothing can be touched," Miss Slessor explained, pushing her hair back from her damp, hot forehead. She had looked down at the box in her arms and added sorrowfully, "One of them is no longer alive, but I think we will save the other."

When Mary left, the living twin was being raised, along with many other native children who had been abandoned by their parents for one reason or another, in Miss Slessor's home. One child Mary remembered particularly well because she was so pretty. Her ears were flat and beautifully shaped, her eyes huge and sorrowful, and her skin smooth and free of sores. That child, Miss Slessor had told Mary with profound satisfaction, had been found in the bushes beside the path leading from the village. The mother had died in childbirth and no one wanted to be bothered to take care of the baby.

A soft, heavy fragrance wafted out from shore where

delicate sprays of moon-glimmering flowers hung from the trees. Mary wiped the perspiration from her forehead with the back of her sleeve. Even on deck the air was warm. It was warmer here than it had been in Calabar—but now she was in Equatorial Africa and it was June. Day and night were both mercilessly hot and wet, with temperatures sometimes going as high as 120° Fahrenheit. Also, the *Mové*, like most African river boats, burned native mahogany for fuel, chunks of it being purchased from villagers who waited along the shore. The light from this wood fire polished the perspiring faces and bare chests of the Krumen stokers to a shining bronze. From where Mary stood she could see into the engine room's stoke hole and she marveled at the African's ability to endure heat.

From above the engine room, the white engineer shouted to the stokers, "Make fire more small! Small small!"

They were slowing down in order to drop anchor. A second engineer, this time a native, came up out of the engine room. He paused beside Mary, gesturing toward the river. *"Nu hie ye felo si ehii mli wo,"* he said.

The man seemed to resemble the tribes around Accra where she had visited briefly, but the dialect was unfamiliar to her. She shook her head sadly, touching her lips to indicate her lack of understanding.

From the railing, the white engineer volunteered, "He says that the face of the river is beautiful but it's not a good idea to sleep on it—meaning we'd better watch out for dead trees, hippos and other dangers." He added, "We're going to anchor until daybreak. The moon will soon be gone and as our friend here just said, we don't care to run into a sandbank or floating tree in the dark. You won't see much out here, once the moonlight's gone."

He was politely suggesting that she go to bed, Mary

realized. Well, it was time. The four other white passengers, all male, had retired some time ago. There was really little purpose in standing there staring at the landscape, especially when she really needed rest. She said good night to the engineer and left, slapping at the mosquitoes on her clothing to get rid of them before entering her cabin. She seemed to have another slight touch of the fever but there was no point in getting excited about it. A person could not remain long in the tropics without experiencing these chills and temperatures from time to time. She took the quinine prescribed for the symptoms and got ready for bed.

The cabin was long and narrow, with a single bunk protected by mosquito netting. In such heat, even the mosquito netting seemed to shut out any wisp of air—and her own rising temperature did not help. Mary unlaced her boots and took off her black cap. As she removed her hairpins, she put them carefully inside a small box. Hairpins were hard to come by in Africa. She had already lost a good many, mostly because they slid from her hair when she bent over her fish net or got dunked in the water accidentally.

Established under the mosquito netting, she knew she could not immediately go to sleep, so she began a letter to Dr. Günther at the Museum. Humidity made her hand stick to the paper as she wrote. Beside her bunk was the precious collecting equipment which the Museum had provided for this, her second and more official expedition. The alcohol in which she preserved her specimens added an unpleasant reek to the hot air of the cabin, making her head ache. Nevertheless, she looked at the equipment of science with affection, remembering Günther's praise.

"Frankly," he had said, "I had no idea you would do so well. Some of these specimens have never been studied scientifically before. Your good judgment in deciding what to collect is amazing."

And yet, she thought, she had not given her whole mind to collecting. Procuring fish and beetles and rare snakes was still only a part of her real interest in this land. Now, as she wrote to Günther of her plans to go to still wilder country upstream, she found herself thinking more of the anthropological research she could do there than of capturing scaly or buzzing creatures.

A mosquito whined against the netting. Mary put her letter aside. She felt a little more relaxed now and perhaps she could sleep.

Quiet settled over the boat. Through the quietness came the sounds of the African night. Home, she thought again. A home filled with the cry of monkeys, the grunt of a hippopotamus, the scratchings of birds and small creatures. A symphony. Perpetual music. Drowsy rhythms . . .

When she woke up it was to the sound of a musical pattern of speech. "Fix a one. Come now. Hey, I not catch." The crew was up and busy about the duties connected with getting the ship into motion again. The call for breakfast would soon sound. She got out of bed, carefully examining her clothing for unwelcome six-legged visitors. From the riverbank came the long, soft melody of her favorite birds, the warblers, nestling in the banana trees. The song brushed away the last wisps of sleepiness. She dressed quickly and hurried out on deck.

The forest was now a deep blue-purple against a background of sky changing from yellow to lavender to pink. A few moments more and the sun rose above the long sweep of papyrus reeds growing along the bank. Two thousand years ago the Egyptians had made their writing paper from plants like this, Mary reflected, stirred by the long history of mankind and man's technical progress. All people had once been primitive. Some, with less excuse than the Africans, were still primitive. What was more primitive than war?

The sun continued its climb, dispersing the river mists until only bits of the vapor remained in the shadows between trunks of trees. As the mists evaporated, the tsetse flies appeared. They came swarming up from the sides of the steamer with silent deadliness, winging hopefully to the dark skins of the perspiring crew for a breakfast of blood. A trader had told her that the tsetse did not like whiteness because it made him too visible to enemies. Whether that was true or not, the dangerous fly was responsible for the dreadful African sleeping sickness.

Brushing at the flies, Mary walked back and forth, watching the sun's promise fade behind rain-threatening clouds. The Ogowé scarcely needed more water in its great channel, she thought wryly. It was the greatest river between the Niger and the Congo and ought to be satisfied. As the steamer rounded a bend, she saw again the climbing plants that had made the air so fragrant last night. The vines had bell-shaped, bright-colored flowers and formed curtains between trees as wide as forty feet and from thirty to sixty feet high in places. Many of the tree trunks were white, mottled with pink lichen and crimson fungus.

It was late afternoon when the ship's whistle sounded and Mary saw a trading post appear.

Mr. Hudson, agent-general for Hatton and Cookson's trading firm, joined her on deck. "That's Woermann's post," he said, pointing. "Beyond that is Government House and then the next building is our factory."

The engineer yelled into the stoker room. "Tom-Tom!

Haul out some of them fire and open them drains one time."

"Yes, sah!" The African firemen hooked the glowing wood from the fire and threw it out on the iron deck in front of the furnace door, dousing the wood with water. The *Mové*, her fires dying, came slowly to a stop and was moored to a tree near shore.

"Well, here we are," Mr. Hudson said, escorting Mary to the trading post's broad verandah. "I see the young French pastor from the mission station is here. Perhaps you can go in his canoe to Lambaréné to talk to the Jacots about staying with them for a while." He found her a chair and then left her to hunt up the firm's Ogowé agent.

Watching the agent-general walk off, Mary felt gratitude for his courtesy and helpfulness. It would certainly be a relief if the missionaries at Lambaréné, Mr. and Mrs. Jacot, would agree to let her headquarter there.

She slapped at her neck. The mosquitoes were thick, their whine an undercurrent to the sound of the cicadas and frogs and, overhead, the whistle of the parrots flying into the great trees, their tails spread wide. A canoe slipped past the bank in front of her, the crew singing. Mary felt a lift of pleasure, despite the mosquitoes, at the sound.

The next day Mary secured a ride to the mission station around a curve of the bay. The Jacots welcomed her warmly, though they had very little room to spare in the mission house which stood like a small citadel against the encroachments of the French Congo jungle. This mission at Lambaréné, where Dr. Nassau had first ministered and taught the Africans, was the same one to which Dr. Albert Schweitzer was to come twenty years later, in 1913. Here he would build his world-famous hospital at the edge of the virgin forest. He would be treating patients from the same Igalwa and Fan and other tribes that Mary Kingsley visited and traveled with and treated from her own limited medical knowledge and supplies.

One of Madame Jacot's first warnings to Mary was "You must be careful, mam'selle, in your dealings with the Fans. They're cannibals, you know."

Mary knew. She had seen the Fans around the Gaboon Estuary farther north. They had struck her as being the handsomest natives she had ever seen, being lighter in color than the other coast tribes, and strong and well-made. But they had their fierce aspect, with their blackened and filed teeth, their hair plaited with copper rings or white beads, huge knives suspended over their shoulders, and so many fetishes hung around their necks and arms that they rattled as they walked. All of them carried guns. "I'm always careful," she assured her hostess, knowing as she said it that her idea of being careful and that of Madame Jacot might not be identical. She could not carry out her work without going among the Fan, and besides, they aroused her interest and curiosity. Some of the Indians her father had run into in the United States had not been exactly gentle, from the stories he had told. Adventure and pursuit of knowledge in untamed places involved certain risks.

Mary set off one morning through the bush—the African forest—her only weapon a bowie knife which she had fastened to the belt of Charles' trousers under her usual full skirts. Her revolver had been left with the French customs at Gaboon, because the duty she would have to pay to bring it with her was too high. Knives and revolvers were not the weapons she counted on. Her real weapons were the trinkets and tobacco she carried in the deep pockets of her skirt. To Madame Jacot's warnings about snakes, Mary answered that she had already discovered that a cleft stick was the ideal weapon against them. Her collection of snake skins proved this later.

The forest seemed deserted except for a few chattering monkeys, but Mary went cautiously, keeping an eye out for gorilla tracks. Bees buzzed warningly as she passed a hollow tree. Bee trees were treasure troves to the natives, who smoked out the insects and then devoured the honey, wax, dead bees, worms, dirt and all.

An object resembling an elephant-hide shield lay on the side of the trail a few yards ahead. Curious, Mary took several steps toward it, following a sloping side path thick with undergrowth. Suddenly this path fell out from under her and she went crashing downward straight through the roof of a native hut. She realized dazedly that the hut must have been built in a hollow below a bank so that it was not visible from above.

She pulled herself together. Encircling her were several startled Fans, men, women and children. The men were naked except for a garment about the middle made from the soft inside bark of a tree, over which hung the skin of some wild animal. The women wore even less. Like the men, their teeth were filed and their skin was daubed with red dye. One carried a baby on her back in a tree-bark sling.

No one said anything. Mary's mind drummed with the advice a Coaster had given her: "No matter how afraid you are, never show it."

She brushed away the leaves and sticks clinging to her clothing, vainly trying to think of some word of Fan language. One of the men burst out with some rapidly-delivered phrases but Mary, not knowing if the words were friendly or hostile, made no effort to reply. Before any of the others could join in, she reached into her skirts for the trade articles. Silence fell again as the Fans watched her, their eyes suspicious.

She pulled out three pocket handkerchiefs, hoping that her hands did not tremble as she handed them and a head of tobacco to the Fans nearest her. Her hand closed on a small knife in her right pocket and she hesitated—but after a moment, this, too, was brought out and presented to her probably unwilling hosts.

The natives grew excited but now there was a lessening of tension. They seized the gifts and began talking to each other, gesturing and pointing at Mary. She stepped back, making herself smile and shaking her own two hands together to indicate her good will. If she were to be eaten, she told herself, she might as well be cheerful about it.

The Fans were clearly more interested in their tobacco than anything else at the moment. They soon had their pipes going and even the children were allowed a few puffs. Between puffs, everyone chattered. The man who had first spoken pushed forward another younger man who haltingly got out the words, "Berrah fine dash, sah," to Mary. A dash, Mary knew, was a present, something not to be paid for. As for her being addressed as "sah," that might be thanks to Charley's trouser cuffs peeking out from under her skirt.

"You're welcome," she said, hoping it was apparent in her voice how welcome the Fans were to anything she had if they would just let her get away from there. Boldly she backed toward the door opening. One of the women reached out and felt her skirt and a youngster touched her shoes with an expression of amazement on his face. With a nervous impulse to laughter, Mary realized that he probably thought the thick leather of the boots was her actual skin.

The young Fan who had managed the few words of trade

English followed her from the hut. Gesturing with his gun, he pointed out a path for her to take. Mary "dashed" him with another small gift, turned, and walked away with as much dignity as she could muster.

Once out of sight of the hut, she stopped and leaned weakly against a tree until her nerves quieted. She decided not to tell the Jacots about her little adventure. She was depending on Monsieur Jacot to help her with her plans for explorations farther up the river and since nothing worse than a few scratches and a bruise had resulted from her unexpected visit to the Fans, it was not wise to worry her hosts. Monsieur Jacot had said he would arrange her passage ninety miles upriver to N'jolé, the last port for the river steamers and the end of European settlements for five hundred miles. From N'jolé on, other plans would have to be made.

On June 22, Mary set off on the *Éclaireur*, a stern-wheeler which made regular trips to N'jolé. As the steamer slowly made its way between low banks, the forest on either side was broken only by village clearings where open, thatched huts seemed in danger of being swallowed up by armies of trees. Fan villages and white men's factories and occasional plantations alternated with patches of land covered only with egombie-gombie trees. The presence of these umbrellalike trees, uniform in height and with large leaves growing in a cluster at the top of a straight stem, meant there had once been a village where they grew. This information came from a trader, Mr. Cockshut, who also traveled on the *Éclaireur*.

"When Africans get a notion that a witch has stolen into a village," he said, "they pick up and move the whole village. The egombie-gombie tree springs up in the bare spot to cover the ground until slower-growing trees rise once more. The natives are very superstitious."

What was superstition? Mary reflected. For the African, belief in witches and evil spirits was part of his religion. The idea of a good and loving God had not been part of it, although there were good and bad spirits in which he believed. She felt a need to respect all forms of religion, no matter how remote from her own. All men, it seemed to her, whether black or white, red or yellow, yearned for God; it was only that they did not agree who or what God is.

Her father had contended, in their discussions, that cannibalism was a religion and ought to be treated as such by Europeans. It was obvious that Europeans could not encourage such religions, but neither could they treat cannibalism as criminal, when it was not against the laws of the tribes who believed in it. Fans and some other tribes believed that by eating their dead relatives they could acquire some of the traits possessed by the dead. It would take education and patience, not force, to change this belief.

The Talagouga Mission near N'jolé was headed by another Frenchman and his wife, Monsieur and Madame Forget. The Forgets welcomed Mary as warmly as the Jacots at Lambaréné had, and she was able to collect a sizable lot of fishes different from those she had secured around Lambaréné. This fact made Mary even more determined to go on up the Ogowé, despite the fierce rapids and the lack of any steamer transportation beyond N'jolé.

"I shall just have to learn to handle a native canoe," she declared to her missionary hosts.

She chose a very hot afternoon for her first lesson, while the Forgets were having a siesta. Wandering by herself near the river, admiring the comparative coolness of the scantily-clad natives passing in canoes, Mary saw a few canoes still moored on shore. She chose the smallest of them; the only paddle she could find was a broken one.

Crawling into the bow of the canoe, she shoved off, kneeling in the bottom and steering her unwieldy craft toward a stretch of slack water between the bank and the main current. The canoe slipped along obediently with the thrust of her paddle, and she was just beginning to feel smug about her seamanship when she reached the edge of the slack water. There the current of one of the greatest equatorial rivers in the world took a hand in her affairs. The Ogowé grabbed the canoe and spun it violently. Mission buildings, trees, people, whirled around Mary as she fought vainly with her broken oar. The next instant, the canoe shot downstream, heading straight for a tree which was snagged on a rock in the water. Mary dropped her paddle, reached out, and seized one of the tree's branches, praying that the uprooted tree would not suddenly slip off the rock and carry both her and the canoe to the Atlantic Ocean.

The tree held firm. She managed to work her way back into slack water. With great caution, and humble respect for the skill of the native canoers, she plied the paddle once more, with the sweat streaming down her face and her wrists aching.

Shouts from the shore made her jerk around so swiftly that she shipped water, drenching her clothes. On shore stood Madame Forget, a plantation owner and his wife, and a crowd of school children from the mission. They were waving frantically at her but she had no idea what they were trying to tell her.

A native canoe slid past her stern, the man grinning at her awkwardness as she slowly, stubbornly brought her craft back to the shore. Helping hands reached down to her and she let herself be helped out of the canoe.

"Oh—oh, Mam'selle!" Madame Forget gasped, shaking her head. "You scared us out of our wits. You can't imagine —I was looking for you and I glanced out and there you were all wound up with a canoe and a dead tree! On the Ogowé!"

Straightening her cap, and holding her wet skirts away from her hostess, Mary said meekly, "I'm sorry to have alarmed you. But you don't know how wonderful it feels to tackle a job like steering a canoe for the first time, and come back safe."

Madame Forget smiled at her enthusiasm and stopped scolding.

Walking back up toward the mission, Mary thought that of all that she had done or might do in life, she would never feel prouder than she did of two special things at this moment. The first was the praise Dr. Günther had given her first fish collection, and the second was her triumph over an Ogowé canoe.

The river at her back made a chuckling sound, and she thought of the rapids farther on. She would not be able to try them alone. And all efforts to hire a crew, so far, had failed. The Africans were afraid of the rapids and the cannibal tribes along the Ogowé's upper reaches. Well, she was, too—but she had to go on. She had not come back to Africa to retreat at the very gates of that unknown wilderness she yearned to penetrate.

✿ CHAPTER EIGHT

AT FIRST, IT SEEMED THAT IF SHE PERSISTED IN GOING ON UP the Ogowé River, she would have to go alone. The Talagouga missionaries shook their heads gloomily.

"It cannot be done," Monsieur Forget said. "You may as well give up."

The owner of a large plantation, neighbor to the mission, Monsieur Gacon, agreed.

Mary Kingsley disagreed. Steadily, she increased the wages, to be paid in food and goods, for a native crew, until finally M. Gacon agreed to spare her one of his canoes and two English-speaking Igalwas who had been part of the way up the fierce river before. "I may be able to complete the crew with six local Fans." At Mary's doubtful look, he added, "They're tamer than their brother Fans up the river."

The Talagouga Fans, however, refused to go above N'jolé at any price. They would certainly be killed and eaten, they declared, by the upriver Fans.

Mary merely grew more determined. By persisting, she finally managed to borrow other Igalwas and M'pongwes from the Hatton and Cookson's factory staff to complete her crew.

With the doleful farewells of her missionary friends echoing in her ears, Mary set out with her native companions. A box of trade goods made a back rest for her, poking at her spine through her clothing. The trade goods constituted her passport through the wild country beyond. As the canoe sliced through the deep, yellow water, she rehearsed the lessons she had been given by friendly traders.

"You have to be what they call a 'devil man,' miss," they had told her. "Those Fans and Bakele will act like devils themselves. They'll want to trade you stuff you have no use for and want you to pay fancy prices for it, at that. And remember that time is forever, for them. Don't try to hurry them, don't let them take over your own quarters, and keep a tight lock on your possessions, especially on dark nights."

As she looked out at the passing scenery, she wondered what her father would think if he could see her now. Would he approve, or would he think this was no job for a woman? There was no way of knowing, she thought with a sigh.

A heron flashed by, his beauty a free gift to anyone who cared to look up and see. She would remember the heron and the lush grandeur of the river banks and her own awareness of them when the time came again for her to leave Africa. She resolved to put down in her notebooks these things and the smattering of information and knowledge she was gaining, in the hope that other students would be helped to understanding by them, someday.

A leaf floated out over the dark river. The voices of the crew cut through her thoughts. One of the English-speaking men, M'bo, stood in front of Mary. As head canoeman, he steered the vessel by yelling at the other paddlers in a kind of singing chant. Behind her "chair," which was her own suitcase with the trade box for a back rest, were two more Africans, paddling, and behind them the other steersman, Pierre. Piled between the trade box and Pierre was the whole party's baggage comprised of pillows, sleeping mats and flowered cotton mosquito nets. As the canoe drew past the end of Talagouga Island, M'bo turned.

"Ah go for poles. Not poles for canoe bery bad up high."

Mary nodded her understanding. They would need strong canoe poles, in addition to the paddles, to get across the Ogowé rapids. Here the river was still peaceful but it would grow wilder and wilder.

The men tied the canoe against the bank of the river near a plantation and jumped out to get the needed poles. It seemed a long time to Mary before they returned and slowly—trying to delay the battle with the rapids as long as possible—started the canoe on its way again.

The river banks grew steeper. Rain started to fall and the canoemen grumbled, dipping their paddles to a slower rhythm.

Impatiently, Mary called to M'bo, "What for so much woe woe?"

"Men say they no got chop. Men all same hungry on riber."

They had bananas but that was not very hearty "chop" for men working so hard in the wet heat. Mary told M'bo that they would get meat or fish as soon as they reached N'jolé and that she had the money to pay for it. As M'bo passed this information on, the faces of the men brightened. M'bo himself struck up a song. The song was made up as it went along, Pierre taking up where M'bo left off, followed by the voices of the other two. Each singer added a bit about himself, his family, or his tribe. Mary felt a familiar pleasure in the sound of their rich and musical voices. The river suddenly seemed a less dangerous place.

Sunlight struggled through the rain clouds. She took her

watch from a small pocket in her blouse. It was eleven o'clock and N'jolé was coming into view. M'bo steered the canoe toward the Dumas trading post, where there was a beach.

On shore, Mary, followed by Pierre, walked up the bright yellow clay road toward the headquarters of the French government. Hedges of pineapple trees guarded acres of coffee bushes alongside the road, and the fragrance of the coffee plant blooms perfumed the air. Off on the other side of the river, Mount Talagouga was a soft, deep blue, and in the middle of the river lay N'jolé Island, low and sandy, with orange trees catching the filtered sunlight. In front of an Igalwa hut near the path a group of Igalwas were making baskets.

Mary presented to the French authorities the letter of introduction Monsieur Forget had given her, but the regular administrator was away and neither of the two Frenchman in charge understood English. Pierre tried to translate.

Nodding toward one of the officials, Pierre said, "He say he no like lady go for rapids. He say no permit lady go. Too dangerous."

"Tell him I must go. Tell him I will be responsible for myself."

Pierre exchanged more words with the Frenchman, then shook his dark head. "He say no. No place for lady up riber."

Mary bit her lip in exasperation. How could she persuade this overchivalrous gentleman to let her through?

"Tell him," she said, "that a lady has been up the Ogowé before, a Madame Quinee! So why not I?"

There was more palaver. The official argued that Madame Quinee had been accompanied by a husband, which made a great difference.

All the hints to travelers she had read had failed to mention the need for a husband while traveling through Africa, Mary thought wryly. Taking a firmer grip on her umbrella, she continued to argue, through Pierre, with the Frenchman. Her life was unimportant to anyone except herself, she said. Furthermore she had a scientific obligation to the British Museum which she was determined to discharge.

The Frenchman took out a handkerchief and wiped his face, muttering something. Finally, he slumped into a chair, waving his hand. If she wanted to kill herself, it was her affair, then. From a cabinet he got out a French flag for her boat and said something more which Pierre interpreted as a hope for luck on her journey.

She had won! Triumphant, Mary took the flag and went to the trading posts to get chop for the crew who by now were beginning to grumble in earnest. The Dumas post, fortunately, had the fish and beef she had promised her men. Mary bought all she could load into the canoe and picked up at the same time some extra knives and cloth for her trade box. It would be disastrous to run out of trade goods after she got into the Fan wilderness.

Marching back to the canoe, she decided that in the future she would tell the authorities that the purpose of her journey was to look for a husband, since she didn't have one!

Mary had a few qualms of her own as the canoe set out once more. She looked back at the French flag, fastened to the canoe, with a feeling of gratitude. She would have no further contact with people of her own race for five hundred miles. That flag and the strange men who made up her crew were all that stood between her and the varied dangers that lurked ahead.

The faces of the crew, plying their leaf-shaped paddles

without enthusiasm, were not reassuring. Their expressions changed from gloom to fear as the river narrowed and the current grew more swift. Masses of black rock began to show on hills and along the shore.

Two hours after they had left N'jolé the first rapids appeared. The sun was strong now, glancing off the grayish masses of bare rock that stood up above the whirling water, each rock a threat to the canoe. Around the sinister rocks the sunlight and spray created a soft blue halo. Small beaches of shining white sand contrasted with the dark green of the forests above the banks.

Cautiously, sweating over their poles, the men tried to hold the canoe close to the right-hand bank where the rapids were less fierce. Then M'bo gave a cry of warning and Mary saw that the canoe was being carried toward a jut in the bank. Behind her, Pierre was fighting vainly with his pole to hold the canoe back.

The rock wall rushed forward. Other rock grazed the canoe's side.

"Jump for bank, sah!" M'bo yelled at Mary, the whites of his eyes flashing.

It was easier said than done. Reaching up, she managed to grasp a knob of stone. Then, feeling like a clambering insect, she hung against the rock wall while she fought for a footing. Strong hands pushed from below as Pierre leaped out in turn. Then, scratching at the bank with fingernails and shoe leather, she managed to pull herself up to safety. Below, the rest of the crew, splashing about in the rapids, frantically worked to hold the canoe steady while they grappled with the chain on its prow. Pulling mightily, they managed to drag the craft around the point to safer waters.

A few minutes more and they were all on their way

again—until the next point of rock sent Mary jumping for a bank once more.

By late afternoon she felt numb from her bruises, but whenever the crew showed any reluctance to go on, she firmly ordered them to keep paddling. Soon, she reminded M'bo, they ought to reach the Fan village he knew of, whose members he trusted. Then they all could rest.

The sun was still shining when they reached the village. Mary, measuring the amount of daylight left, thought of the extra miles they could cover if they didn't stop. She ordered M'bo to keep the canoe moving—surely they could find another village a little farther on.

M'bo pretended not to hear and steered directly for shore. "Ah find out many tings," he said, clambering out to meet the Fans who were gathering on shore and staring at Mary and the canoe.

Everyone talked at once. Mary, watching from the canoe, gathered that they were all paying each other compliments. This was heartening. One of the Fans, wearing a feathered cap, his body held erect in a kingly manner, ordered everyone to keep still. "*Azuna! Azuna!* Silence! I wish to speak."

M'bo asked the chief which of the villages farther up the river would be the best one in which to spend the night.

The chief picked up a banana leaf, tore it into five different-sized pieces, and laid them on the edge of the canoe at various intervals. The bits of leaf, Mary realized then, represented various villages and their locations. The first leaf was the chief's own village, where they now were, and he made it clear that this was far and away the best place to stop. He eyed the trade box behind Mary as he spoke.

M'bo explained to her that the chief had terrible tales

to tell about most of the other villages. "He say number four not too bad, but rest bery bad, sah."

"We'll risk it." Mary noticed that the chief's eye was fixed more on her person now than on her trade box. She turned around carefully in the easily-capsized canoe and opened the box. All this advice must be paid for, or she and the men would be in trouble. Taking out exactly enough tobacco to go around among the assembled Fans, she handed it to the chief, telling M'bo to give her thanks along with it.

"Now we sing," M'bo announced. He was a convert to Christianity and lost no opportunity to try to convert other natives to his belief. He prodded Pierre and the two of them broke out into a hymn, half in trade English, half in Igalwa, their arms waving enthusiastically. The Fans listened politely and even seemed impressed, although Pierre sang half a line behind M'bo and in a different key.

They left no converts behind them, as far as Mary could tell, but the meeting had stimulated her crew to paddle with such style and vigor that Mary felt the village Fans would think twice before following them or making any attempt to attack them.

Sand bars and rocky points passed in swift procession. Mary was becoming so adept at the art of jumping to the safety of a bank on a second's notice, and her companions applauded her skill with such enthusiasm, that she began to wonder if they were deliberately steering toward the rocks to provide entertainment for themselves.

They passed village number two, and then number three. The current grew more fierce and daylight was fading into gloom. Anxiety became Mary's extra companion as she searched for signs of village fires in the growing darkness but saw only the channel of the river, looking as though made of melted iron, around every bend. When the last bit of afterglow had gone, the sky turned to purple velvet jeweled with huge stars. Millions of fireflies clustered over the river and along the shore. In the brown stretches of river ahead, there were sudden flashes of starlit foam, warning of more rapids beyond. But the only warning against fallen trees in the boat's path was the *"lish-swish"* of the current flowing through their branches. In the clutch of roaring rapids, the *lish-swish* was drowned out and the canoe crashed blindly into the fallen trees.

Crash, swish, crackle! A tree bough lurched out of the darkness and pressed against Mary's chest, lifting her halfway out of the canoe, ripping at her clothing and her hair.

"How much more far?" she cried at M'bo and Pierre when she had escaped the rough embrace of the branches.

They shook their heads. They did not know.

No one knew. There was nothing to do but forge onward in the hope of finding Fans friendly enough to let them share a fire and shelter for the night.

Groping outward, searching the shore for the sign of a blaze, they struck rapids that were the worst so far. Then rocks scraped at the canoe's bottom. They were so numerous that for a moment Mary had the conviction that the crew had steered it onto land. The canoe shuddered to a halt, jammed among the rocks. While the men worked with poles to free the craft, Mary seized an extra paddle. Just as she thought they had worked free, more rocks and rushing current caught the canoe. She felt the vessel turn, rearing like an animal. It tilted, quivering, and dumped crew and cargo into the foaming water.

At some moment in the wild scramble to put things to rights, Mary found herself clinging to the overturned canoe, her hair streaming, the water surging around her, and the

95

whole vast sky looking down at her. The stars must be blinking in astonishment, she thought, at the spectacle of an English woman hanging onto the edge of a native canoe in the froth of one of Africa's wildest rivers, with only four dusky semisavages as her companions. The four valiantly righted the canoe and helped her to climb aboard once again and she thought how each mishap, each shared risk, made her and her guides less afraid of each other, more willing to accept the other's basic human similarity. With relief and gratitude, she watched as they rescued the precious trade box and the rest of the cargo, including her fishing bottles, before climbing into the canoe to take up their paddles.

When, once again, the canoe became wedged between rocks, she gave the order to haul the canoe to shore and try their luck on land. Gorillas and boa constrictors were no greater menace to tired men than the whirlpools and rocks of the river.

Stumbling wearily through a rocky, matted forest, carrying their cargo with them, they stopped finally at M'bo's cry of "Fire make light—there!"

Mary peered ahead, trying to glimpse the gleam. In a few minutes she heard the steady, hollow beat of a drum.

A village appeared in a clearing, the houses built along a street about sixty feet long. The huts were very low and built of palm mats. Before each hut a fire burned, the flames illuminating the lean, leaping figures of dancers. The red light of the fires accentuated the red paint on the dancers' bodies. Mary stopped, her pulses drumming. She was staring straight into the red heart of savagery! But wasn't this what she had come so far to see and hear? With M'bo beside her, she went forward, the rest of the crew following. At first, they were not noticed by the assembled crowd. The drummer, a gray-haired man, kept pounding his long, high, black and white drum with vigor. The dancers went on dancing, their bare feet slapping the earth in time to the drum. These people, she thought, did not look like Fans.

M'bo announced his presence but even then the dancers scarcely paused and the drummer kept on at his task. Mary's fears lightened. The villagers were not very much interested in her and her party; M'bo had a difficult time making the drummer stop pounding long enough to tell him where there might be a place for the white visitor to sleep. Finally, the drummer got up and led the way to a broken-down building of bare poles partially roofed with palm-thatch and enclosed by odds and ends of palm-thatch walls. Two smoky torches, propped against a stone, provided light, and a hollowed scrap of tree trunk served as a cupboard.

Outside, the crew's cook went about the business of preparing chop at an open fire. Mary, waiting for the food, saw that a number of natives had followed her and were now crowding into the hut. Among them were two men who claimed to be chiefs. They wore cast-off white men's clothing—old French military coats in rags. What clothes the other men had were even more ragged. Obviously, these natives had known white people before. Haltingly, she tried to speak to them and, after some struggle, found that they called themselves Adoomas. They had once had a better village but the Fans had taken it. The French had reclaimed it for them but in the meantime their banana plantation had suffered and they had lost many of their possessions.

After accepting gifts from the trade box, they finally left, and Mary was able to eat in solitude the food the crew's cook brought her. Soon afterward she heard M'bo holding a

97

Christian worship service for the Adoomas, followed by the beat of drums once more, and the thumping of dancing feet.

When, finally, M'bo and Pierre came to the hut to help her tidy it up for the night, she left them briefly to escape the smell of the bush light torches in the hut, as well as the heavy air inside the hut. Standing by the river, she found it hard to decide which was more brilliant, the moon rising above the trees or the legions of fireflies. On every side, the peaks of the Sierra del Cristal rose out of the half-light, catching the glow of the low moon. But the foaming, flying Ogowé was still dark in its cavern, only an occasional gleam and the sound of its thunder revealing its presence.

She leaned against a rock pinnacle, drinking in the scene, marveling again as she so often did at how such places as this had the power to remove everything from her mind except a deep awareness of peace. All human concerns and anxiety, even the deep grief she still felt for her dead parents, fell from her. These trees, this moon, the shining mountain peaks, rocks and foam—all became part of herself and the peace within her.

When she went back to the hut, where M'bo had arranged a bed for her on a wooden bench and hung a mosquito net over it, she lit a candle and put it on her suitcase beside her bed. Taking her damp, dilapidated copy of Horace under the net with her, she read until her eyelids sagged.

She went to sleep to the sounds of rats rustling around among the huts—and awoke to find herself on the ground. Looking up at the wooden bench from which she had fallen, she wondered if she would not be better off on the bare earth. The memory of the rats she had seen in other native villages sent her climbing back onto her hard bed again, however. She must try to get back to sleep. If the journey tomorrow to the island of Kondo Kondo, where she planned to collect more fish, was as rugged as this day's travels had been, she would need all the energy she could store up.

The journey upstream to the island proved to be as bad as the first day's journey had been, but Mary's party reached the island safely. Now she was able to get on with the official purpose of this particular expedition, fish collecting. The only real terror she felt along the way was near a cave into which the river plunged at one point, the Boko Boko. She had heard the cave described by various people and the sight of its black portals filled her with a peculiar dread.

"Plenty, plenty bats, hedgehogs and snakes live," Pierre said solemnly, peering into the depths of the cave.

Mary shuddered. Compared with the aspect of this hole, the Fan tribes seemed no threat at all. She had no intention of exploring the cave.

A memorable experience of quite another kind was the night spent on Kondo Kondo—a night of more stars and moon, following a sunset so brilliant it seemed that the whole horizon was aflame. That night her crew seemed to have lost their gloom and fear. Even the routine upsets on the rapids became funny in the many retellings. They were becoming almost jolly. Even if their merriment left them on the journey back down the Ogowé by a different route, Mary felt certain now that there would be a journey back. She had not been sure of that fact during much of the up-river struggle.

She imagined herself returning the French flag—intact except for its many drenchings—to the worried French officials at Talagouga. It would be more intact than her own clothing, she thought, looking at her ripped and patched skirts and her poor, sunfaded cap. Only her determination was still whole.

Standing under the Kondo Kondo moon, she found herself distracted even from the beauty around her by the nagging desire for other journeys, more knowledge. In the forests and mangrove swamps or on the slopes of the gleaming mountains, other unknown tribes and customs beckoned to her hungry, adventurous mind.

She remembered with sadness the forlorn knife and leopardskin loin cloth which she and Pierre had found wedged among the rocks of the island at the edge of some tremendous falls. The articles were silent evidence that the Alemba falls had claimed at least one victim. But when she slowly made her way back to camp, she was trying to recall the lines from one of Rudyard Kipling's poems that said everyone had to die sometime, somewhere; what was important was how one lived. Equally important was that one felt alive. Before, she had been a ghost in a house of memories. Now . . . The moonlight on her face was blinding in its radiance. She had told Charles that she preferred nonhuman things to human ones and the moonlight touching her so lightly was surely one of those nonhuman loves. But she was, to her own deep satisfaction, also acquiring something close to a feeling of love for the unsophisticated black men with whom she had by now spent most of her time in Africa. They accepted her, not as one of themselves—they were fully aware of the differences between them and her—but at least as a fellow human being, one to be trusted and liked. Friends are where you find them, she thought.

CHAPTER NINE

BACK AT LAMBARÉNÉ AGAIN, MARY CONTINUED HER ATTEMPTS to learn to handle a native canoe. Most of her efforts were more amusing than dangerous and eventually she began to feel she could compete with the natives if it proved necessary. She also used the time to study the Fan language, with Monsieur Jacot's help. The missionary was compiling a dictionary of Fan words. Jacot, of French parentage, had been born in America and was well educated. Mary spent many hours discussing the problems and future of Africa with him. And on some of the warm evenings, Jacot and his wife sat on the verandah, singing old French, Swiss and English songs in their rich, full voices, while a crowd of silent natives crept close to listen.

Although Mary felt great warmth and sympathy for all the people of Africa, it was the African children who touched her heart most deeply. So many of them, looking out upon the world with strangely sad, questioning eyes, seemed to be asking whether there was really any place for them in the world. Four times out of ten, the answer was no and the little ones died. Not enough food of the right kind, diseases, sores, and lack of medical care were among the causes. Her own nursing skill, or that of the missionaries, was no match for the death that stalked the jungles and rivers in many forms. It was even more tragic to see how quickly the children learned who did survive and attended the mission schools—but then, when they grew too old for the school or moved away from its influence, there was nothing for them to do and no new lessons to learn except the cruel lessons of survival in the African bush.

Mary was invited to visit the home of one of the Igalwa families whose children came to the Jacots' mission school. The Igalwa was a dying-out coastal tribe and she felt it particularly important for her to find out all she could of their customs for the anthropological record.

The village where the family lived was at the upriver end of Lambaréné Island, the largest island on the Ogowé, about fifteen miles long, a mile to a mile and a half wide. The island's rocky hills were forested in most places, and small streams ran down the hills into the river. The Ogowé began to separate there into a network of channels which carried its waters one hundred and thirty miles to the Atlantic Ocean.

Since the Jacots' mission was on the mainland, Mary went to the island by canoe. She ran into some rough water but managed to land without capsizing. With her umbrella in hand and a notebook in her pocket along with merchandise from the trading post, she followed a path from the beach and in a few minutes found herself walking down a clean, sandy street bordered by men and women sitting on the bare ground. Some of them were mending fishing nets but most of them merely sat. The Igalwas, familiar with the sight of members of the white race, did not stare as curiously at Mary as the Fans did, and occasionally one of them smiled as she passed by. A woman leading a small child stopped and bending over, said "*Bapika!*" Whereupon the child got onto her back. To Mary the woman said, "Mah pickin," with evident pride. *Pickin* was trade English for child, Mary remembered.

The Igalwa homes were made of bamboo instead of palm thatch. They had windows with wooden shutters and well-carpentered wooden doors, showing the greater influence of the Europeans on them compared with the wilderness tribes. Inside the house to which she had been invited, Mary was offered a chair by the table so that she could put her umbrella and notebook down. The Igalwas had slaves living in a separate village at the other end of the island, and they were also prosperous enough to own many items of European manufacture. The chair Mary sat on was a Windsor, and there was a bright tablecloth on the table. In the separate little kitchen, Mary caught a glimpse of European-made saucepans.

"What for you ladies make?" she asked her hostess. Several girls and women were very busy sewing bright-colored patches of cloth together.

Her hostess snatched the biggest swatch of material and held it up in front of Mary. "Dis berrah big cubber for night when cold cold."

It was a patchwork quilt! Shades of my English aunts, Mary thought. She slapped at an ant running across her hand but he had already taken a nip. The ladies all put down their sewing and ran around in great alarm. Mary realized that she must have been bitten by one of the nastier breed of insects. Luckily, she had filled a small bottle with alcohol at the mission and had it in her handbag. Under the interested gaze of her Igalwa friends, she daubed the bite with a clean handkerchief saturated with alcohol, meanwhile asking questions. The ladies told her that this particular ant was a terrible pest and that people sometimes got very sick from its bite. Very encouraging, Mary thought drily, taking a look at her arm. It did not seem to be swelling or getting very red.

Holding the soaked handkerchief over the ant bite, she meanwhile took in everything that went on around her. One of the younger girls was grooming the hair of another. The Igalwas had beautiful hair, very crinkly but fine. It was worn braided close to the head, with many partings between the braids. Into these braids, the ladies stuck pins made from hippo bones, usually one pin on each side of the head.

Mary thought the Igalwa women charming. Their skin, very black, was smooth and free of blemishes, and their figures were gently curved. Most of them had small hands and feet and big brown eyes. Their teeth were as white as the sea surf. When they were dressed for the street, they wore about four yards of cloth draped about them from the armpits downward. A bright shawl was made into a roll and carried on one shoulder. If they were rich enough, the ladies carried a parasol, but not in their hands. The parasol, like the shawl, was purely decorative and was carried rolled up on top of their heads, handle forward. A few of the younger women wore red flowers in their hair.

In stumbling Igalwa, Mary said to her hostess, "You have a nice home and beautiful children."

A smile spread across the dark woman's face and she said, "They are like the child of my mother who lives in the next house. The child of my mother is beautiful."

"Child of my mother" was Igalwa for "my sister," Mary remembered. Her hostess was saying that her daughters were beautiful like her sister who lived in the next house.

When Mary was ready to leave, she asked if there was anyone in the village who could be hired to paddle her back to the mission. She was tired and was not eager to tackle the rough currents again that day.

Much talking and shouting went on, too loud and fast

for her to catch most of it but after a while a man and his wife appeared to offer their services. "Ah name Samuel. Very good man."

Samuel went on to say that he and his wife would take her home in his canoe, leaving Mary's canoe to be fetched back to the mainland later. His price would be "one dollah" for the trip.

Mrs. Samuel was a large, handsome woman, and did most of the paddling on the way home. Mr. Samuel talked. In his high-pitched, thready voice, he began to ask questions of Mary as soon as they set out from the island.

"You be Christian, ma?" he asked.

"Do you know any white person who isn't Christian?" she countered.

"Yes, ma."

"Well, keep away from them," Mary said.

"Yes, ma."

There was silence for a time, except for the steady dip of Mrs. Samuel's paddle and an occasional boost from her husband's, also.

Then Samuel asked, "Where be your husband, ma?"

"I no got."

"No got!" This was said in such a loud, shocked tone that Samuel's wife jerked the canoe in fright, almost tipping him into the river. Water from the paddle splashed over both him and Mary.

Samuel shook the water off himself and repeated, "No got husband, ma?" as if he could not believe his ears.

Mary, smiling to herself, tried to change the subject by asking about the rubber trade but Samuel brushed her question off with, "I no be trade man. Why you no got husband?"

Mary sighed. In the Ogowé district, women were highly

prized. The more wives a man had, the richer he was. She could easily understand that any woman who could get no husband at all, in such a society, must seem like a very poor creature to Samuel. She shook her head at him, to indicate she would not answer any more questions.

That evening at supper she told the Jacots about her canoe ride with the Samuels. "Yes, the natives here do have a high regard for women," Monsieur Jacot said. "Their laws, which I sometimes find a bit exasperating, are an advantage for a woman like yourself traveling alone. If a West African so much as brushes against a woman who does not belong to him, he can be sued for all he owns. So they are all quite careful not to risk any such event."

She had certainly been treated with respectful friendliness on that trip up the Ogowé River rapids, Mary thought. Tribal law, however, was not the only reason, in her opinion. The truth was that the Africans in the interior did not really think of her as a woman, despite her skirts and her long hair. Most of them addressed her as "sah" once she was away from the coast and the mission areas, instead of the "ma" that Samuel had used.

"You may make any explanation you can think of, next time you see Samuel," she said to Monsieur Jacot with mischief in her voice, "about my husbandless plight."

The dry season was slowly coming to Lambaréné. The banks across from the mission, which a few weeks earlier had been covered with water, were turning now to golden sand. The children kept track of the season by sticking a large palm frond into the sand bank at its highest point, while the bank was still under water. Each day more and of the palm's stem showed. When the whole frond became visible, the boys and girls clapped and sang with delight. Then canoeloads of young people went to the sand to swim or wash clothes in the clear water at its edge, and on moonlight nights dancers with bush-light torches flitted about like fireflies.

Even Madame Jacot, too busy to play, took her work out to the verandah when it was possible. "It's such a relief when that sand shows up," she said to Mary. "It's the only bare, dry ground I see all year. After a few weeks, when the rains start again, it disappears, and then all we see from here is water and forest."

To Mary the forest was still mysteriously inviting, full of adventure and secrets she yearned to discover, but she was able to understand the missionary wife's feelings. The job of being a missionary in this part of the world was not easy. Their lives were hard and lonely. The Jacots, she thought with admiration, must have a profound belief in the value of their work, to stay on year after year. Had they found themselves, as she hoped to do, by losing themselves in their work?

One of the hardest jobs the missionaries had to do was to run the store that was part of the mission station. The store at Lambaréné was not operated with the idea of buying and selling for profit; it was more like a bank. Monsieur Jacot and evangelists trained by him often had to make journeys among the wilder tribes. It was necessary to get supplies along the way and some kind of system of payment must be set up, since carrying enough trade merchandise along would be difficult. A printed paper resembling a check and called a "book" was given as payment for food or services. A native could, when he came to Lambaréné, turn this "book" in at the mission store for merchandise.

Watching Monsieur Jacot operating the store one day, Mary wondered, as she had before, at his patience. An Igalwa was staring into a box of fishhooks, fingering the hooks with care, scratching his stomach as he tried to decide if a fishhook was what he really wanted most. Several other natives, some of them Fans, were admiring some lengths of cloth that Madame Jacot had draped across a table and a younger Fan was trying to slip one of the store's supply of hunting knives inside his loin cloth.

"Let's have that knife, Egaja!" Monsieur Jacot called out sharply, in Fan. "Put it back where you found it."

With loud protests that he had no intention of stealing the knife but was only admiring it, the Fan reluctantly put it back in its box on the counter.

Mary chose a few items for her trade box. As she took out her money to pay Monsieur Jacot, she noted that her supply of funds was getting ever slimmer. She would have to sharpen her trade wits if she was to stretch her merchandise enough to see her through the journey she was planning. It was a journey never before taken by a white woman, going overland from the Ogowé River north to the Rembwé and thence down to Gaboon on the coast.

"I've four Ajumba for your crew," Monsieur Jacot told her when he had finally got all of his customers to make up their minds and had closed the store for the day. "They've promised to be ready at dawn." He locked the door of the store and ushered Mary ahead of him along the path to his house. "I wish you weren't going but I know we can't stop you."

"I'll turn up again like all bad pennies," Mary assured him. They had argued this all out before. The Jacots plainly never expected to see her again.

The four Ajumbas did not arrive at dawn as promised but they did arrive at eight, in pouring rain. Mary, her umbrella over her, stepped into the canoe Monsieur Jacot had secured for her journey, and took her usual place in the middle of the vessel. She had a very bad headache and tried to get rid of it by resting on the luggage while the crew maneuvered the canoe around the island to a village where they were to procure yams and bananas to add to their food supplies. They loaded the yams and went on.

The headache subsided a little after a while and Mary sat up to take a closer look at the four men who were to be her sole companions on this long and dangerous journey.

One of the men was very gentlemanly-looking. He was wearing a gray shirt, so because his name was difficult to pronounce Mary nicknamed him Grey Shirt. The second man she gave the name of Singlet, because of the jersey undershirt which was his main costume. Singlet and Grey Shirt were Christians, according to the Jacots, but the other two were pagans. All four men had a friendly look, Mary decided, and then forgot about them as the canoe hit a sand bank and came to a stop. The yams that had just been loaded had to be thrown onto the shore so the men could push the canoe off the bank. Afterward they waded back to pick the yams up again and reload. Such accidents happened often, so that the canoe arrived at its first stop, the village of Arevooma, barely before nightfall.

Arevooma was Grey Shirt's home. Mary was escorted to his house at the west end of the town and welcomed by his pretty coffee-colored wife. Tea was brought to her on the verandah on a table adorned with a calico tablecloth. The tea was very welcome and a help in ridding herself of the remnants of her headache. Sleep, she felt, would help even more. As soon as Grey Shirt and his wife left her for the night, she began to wash her face, feeling almost as relaxed and comfortable as if she were still at the mission. The bed, she noticed gratefully, was covered with mosquito netting and had clean calico covers and patchwork pillows.

Mary had just removed two of her hairpins when a step was heard on the verandah. A man's voice called, "Are you dere, ma?"

Mary quickly put the pins back and swept up any other loose strands. She was still completely dressed.

Her visitor was a native evangelist, Ndaka, from the Jacots' mission. He had come to Arevooma to settle his dead brother's estate, he explained.

"Ndaka is holding big song, maybe one, two, tree song, outside," he said. It was dark by then and he carried a lantern which waved about as he gestured with it. He had come to invite her to attend his meeting, presumably a religious one.

Mary wanted to refuse but Ndaka was an associate of the Jacots and it would be a discourtesy to them if she did, headache or not. She let Ndaka escort her to the center of the village and find a seat for her in the row of people already gathered to hear him.

Perched uneasily on a native stool, Mary had a hard time following the open-air service. It was with relief that she found herself, after an hour or more, back again in Grey Shirt's house. The atmosphere outdoors was forty-five per cent sold matter in the shape of mosquitoes but she had managed to get rid of most of them at the door. She crawled under the mosquito netting around the bed and, with Grey Shirt's cat at her feet, fell asleep almost at once. Once she woke up to the sound of crashing china. The cat was gone but a little while later it came back, purring and kneading Mary's stomach. It had killed a rat and wanted to be congratulated for its work—but luckily Mary did not realize this until morning.

It was grey dawn when Mary awoke the second time.

Grey Shirt was knocking so loudly on the door that two centipedes and a scorpion dropped from the mosquito net onto the bed. Bouncing them off without touching them, she realized they had probably been in the folds of the net all night, and this thought propelled her out of bed in a hurry. But her headache was gone at last, and even the discovery that the cat had tipped a basin of water over her suitcase failed to discourage her. She called out to Grey Shirt that she would be ready very soon and that the men should have the canoe ready to travel. Breakfast would not take long.

The broad, quiet waters of this branch of the Ogowé seemed to be a haven for birds. Bright-colored kingfishers made arrow-flights into the river for their breakfasts. Overhead a huge vulture crossed and recrossed above the spot where white cranes and heavy-billed black and white birds resembling puffins waited at the water's edge.

"Dis bird he live for white man fashion," Grey Shirt informed Mary, motioning toward the hornbills, some of which were dodging about in the hippo grass on the river's bank. He went on to explain that the hornbill flocks always had the same number of males and females and thus no male had more than one wife. Whichever lady hornbill the male bird took up with in the beginning was his from that time on, according to Grey Shirt. Mary could see quite clearly from the way Grey Shirt said this that he considered this state of things very unfortunate for Mr. Hornbill. Seeing how interested Mary was in the birds, however, Grey Shirt lifted his paddle and pointed to a tree branch. Three hornbills were perched in a line on the branch, stretched to their full height, their big eyes and huge beaks all open wide. They seemed to be waiting and listening for something. A minute later, Mary heard the peculiar, screeching cry of another hornbill from across the river. All of the birds now began to call back and forth across the river as though discussing the latest hornbill news.

The charts Mary had been given at the Mission Station were not easy to follow, mostly because this country had never been charted by a geographer. Different tribes called rivers and villages by different names; sometimes a river had one name as one traveled upriver and another one coming down.

There were now six men in the canoe. A man who wanted to get work at John Holt's sub-factory on the Rembwé asked to come along as a passenger. He said he had been unable to get to the factory because of "those fearful Fans" along the way.

Alarmed at this news, Mary had asked Grey Shirt, "How are we going to get through if the Fans are so terrible?"

He explained that Pagan had two Fan friends who lived on an island in Lake N'covi and that they would go by that route instead of the more usual one dreaded by the passenger. Fortune favors the brave, Mary told herself, and then wondered just how brave she might turn out to be in a real crisis.

The sixth man was Ngouta, an Igalwa interpreter Mary had taken on at Arevooma.

Each of the men carried his best gun, and all the guns were loaded. The rifles were tied onto the baggage that was Mary's back rest, the muzzles sticking out on either side of her head. Thinking about this as the canoe moved through the water, Mary wondered whether she should find the presence of the artillery comforting or not. It depended on where and how the guns happened to be used!

Turning her thoughts away from such forebodings, she

watched the scenery. The river was so broad here that it looked like a long lake and the broad yellow backs of sand banks were showing, now that the dry season was near. Occasionally, the smoothness of the trip would be interrupted when the canoe was grounded on a dry bank. In the crew's attempt to shove the canoe off into the water, Mary was sometimes tipped in, too. After the first such accident the men tied the cargo into the boat, but no one offered to do the same for Mary.

A beautiful shrub with long bunches of red-yellow and cream-colored young leaves at the end of its branches, called *Obaa* by the Ajumbas, appeared frequently along the river bank; and behind these lower shrubs high green columns marked trees that had been struck by lightning, broken, and covered with climbing vines. Despite wayside accidents the scene seemed luxuriantly lovely to Mary as she watched a gleam of sunshine glance across a red sand bank on the men's rich, red wood paddles. The boatmen were singing their usual detailed story-songs in a minor key, in time to the dip of their paddles, throwing in a line of greeting when the canoe met other canoes, some of them loaded with fruit.

Thinking perhaps that Mary was afraid of drowning when the canoe came close to tipping over on its journey upstream, Pagan comforted her by showing her his "ju ju against drowning." It was shaped like a fire extinguisher, made of iron, and filled with some secret potion. He also carried a red "ju ju for keep foot in path," he assured her. She could only hope that his charms worked for Christians like herself, as well as for him, but she did not rely on it.

The canoe stopped on a sand bank in the Karkola River so that its occupants could eat some of their food. Mary wandered off to explore her surroundings while the crew smoked their after-dinner pipes. The sand bank was covered with the light, fine, green grass on which hippos and manatees both fed, but behind the grass was a desolate forest. A short way inside the forest she came upon a heap of human bones and remembered that Dr. Nassau, when she visited him in Liberville, had told her that the Ajumbas buried their dead in loose mounds like this in the forest. Despite her interest in religious customs, Mary found the mounds depressing and she went quickly out of the woods to the water's edge.

There, in the water nearest the bank, were thousands of small fish wearing a black line on each side of their tails. They were very tame. She knelt by the edge of the water and fed them crumbs from her hand. At first the larger fish snapped at her fingers, trying to scare away the strange object that had invaded their home territory, but after a few tries, she lured them into swimming right into her palm for the crumbs. She could have caught the fish by handfuls but she already had a specimen like them. She let them swim and feed in peace, content just to watch. Semitransparent yellow spotted sandfish with cup-shaped fins in front were there, too, but they would not take the crumbs.

The river trail took the party into wild and lonely country, growing wilder and lonelier each hour they traveled it. "No white man ever live for this place," Grey Shirt said as they passed a village high on a cliff.

No white person had ever traveled on the Karkola River before, either, he explained. It was with some fear and more respect that he looked at this "sah" who had hired him and his friends to go where white men were supposed to be afraid to go. On an island in the river was a little white hut which, the men told Mary, had once been occupied by a black trader for John Holt's company. It looked desolate to Mary and she imagined crocodiles and hippos coming up at night on the ground surrounding it.

Another sand bank island covered with sword grass ten feet high appeared at the side of the canoe. Watching a path through the grass as the canoe glided past, Mary saw a hippo get to his feet about six feet from her. He stared at her a minute or two, then yawned, opening his mouth wide enough to swallow her.

"Oh, oh, look what's happening!" she said to Singlet, who was closest to her. The hippo had grunted the news of their presence out to the rest of his herd. Like a fleet of trucks, they began moving toward the river.

Ai yi! Yi, yi, yi!" This howl came from The Passenger. Ngouta, the interpreter, dropped to the bottom of the canoe to make mumbling sounds of fright. The Ajumbas, silent, dipped their paddles with nervous speed into the water, sending the canoe to the opposite side of the river.

Mary was as anxious to leave the hippos behind as her crew was. She couldn't decide whether Nature had made the hippos before she had learned how to create beauty or whether it was the other way around. Perhaps, she thought, Nature got tired of making delicate and graceful creatures like the antelope, coralline, and butterflies, and just decided to put whatever scraps of material she had left lying around into big bags—the hippopotamuses.

To get out of sight of the hippos, the men took the canoe down a narrow channel between semi-island sand banks. This turned out to be only a little less dangerous than the hippo area, because the sand banks were occupied by crocodiles. They were evidently taking their midday siestas, Mary decided, eyeing their wide-open mouths with considerable nervousness. One ancient creature must have been a grandmother, because so many lively young crocs were running all over her.

Pagan and Silence wrinkled up their noses to indicate their disgust with the heavy smell of these river beasts and they did not linger near the banks. Poles were thrust into the river bottom to boost the canoe along as silently and rapidly as possible. When they were safely beyond the crocodile encampment, Mary asked if there were many gorillas, elephants, or bush cows around this part of the country. She might as well know the worst at once, she felt.

Pagan answered her grimly. "Plenty too much," he said.

In England, Mary thought with a sharp pang of home-sickness, the corn would be turning a gold-green. She remembered that she was supposed to be a scientist, one particularly interested in river creatures. One of her scientist friends had said to her before she started for Africa, "Always take measurements, Miss Kingsley, and take them from the adult male. Some collectors are content with a guess but it's not scientific."

Turning her head, Mary glanced back in the direction of the two banks they had so quickly fled from. The gray shapes of the crocodiles could barely be distinguished now on the sand. She chuckled to herself as she tried to imagine her crew's faces if she said she had to go back and measure a crocodile.

CHAPTER TEN

THE CANOE SLIPPED ALMOST SOUNDLESSLY ACROSS THE DARK mirror of lovely, lonely Lake N'covi deep in the hushed interior of the continent. The crew's paddles, barely touching the clear water, brought up bubbles of silver. Late afternoon sun, followed by sunset flushes and the spreading afterglow, turned the forest hills to purple and blue. In spite of its almost incredible beauty, there was something frightening about the scenery and Mary had to control a shiver. The place gave off an air of evil, as if death lay waiting in the lake depths or along the paths leading up from it to the forest. She straightened up on her suitcase-seat, and thrust back her shoulders, trying to appear nonchalant about what was purely and simply her imagination. Better not let the crew see how ridiculous their "sah" could be, if she wanted to continue her journey with their respect.

Singlet burst out suddenly, "Ah smells blood."

"Don't be a donkey!" Mary snapped, turning her head to glare at him. He had picked her own fear right out of her head, she told herself. She had spoken in her own language and Singlet didn't understand the words but he subsided under the look she had given him.

"He big fool. Go for scare easy, sah." This reproach from Grey Shirt was to reassure Mary but she saw the speaker also glance uneasily at the island they were nearing. He muttered something she did not catch to one of the other

Ajumbas. The canoe's speed was increased, speeding on toward a second island beyond. Mary remembered that Pagan's Fan friend was supposed to be a resident of an island village in this lake. The men must have decided that no friendly beings could inhabit an island that exuded such an air of disaster, and were for that reason going on. Perhaps it was superstition or imagination—but if so, why had she felt it too? It was a puzzle, one she would have to think about later. Meantime, she pretended not to have noticed the haste with which the canoe was leaving the first island.

"What name your friend?" she asked Pagan.

Grey Shirt answered for him. "Name Kiva-Kiva. He be friend me, also."

That was good, Mary thought. She hoped Kiva-Kiva would prove to be her friend as well. They were close to the second island now and a large village could be seen in the distance. Shouts and cries bounced out over the quiet lake.

"Sounds like war," Mary commented.

Her companions only grunted. This was evidently the village of M'fetta, their destination, for they drove the canoe in among outlying rocks. The four Ajumbas moved quickly and quietly, stowing their paddles and slinging on their ammunition bags. Each of them had a loaded gun and as they picked them up they slid the leather sheaths from off the firelocks.

Pagan was the first man out of the canoe. As he stepped onto a stone, the shouting on the bank above suddenly quieted and a crowd of brown-skinned, near-naked Fans poured down the steep cliff toward him.

Every man of the crowd carried a gun and a shovel-shaped knife. As they came closer they unsheathed the knives and Mary, still in the canoe, felt the warning taste of salt in her mouth that indicated fear. Keep your wits about you, Mary Kingsley, she said silently to herself. She gave no sign of her fear but turned to face the oncomers boldly.

The Fans stopped about fifty feet away, motionless and silent.

Grey Shirt now got out of the canoe and joined his friend Pagan. The two held out their left hands but kept their right ones handy to their guns. "Kiva-Kiva!" they shouted. And in native language they added that they had come to see their friend Kiva.

In the canoe, Silence muttered, "It be bad palaver if Kiva no live for this place."

This remark hit Mary hard. It was the first time that the quiet Silence had made any such prophecy of doom.

Ngouta, the interpreter, was staring wild-eyed at the Fans, and The Passenger, who had boasted of his courage, had a pair of badly-shaking knees. Which, Mary thought, did not help the situation. Fans could smell fear even at fifty feet, she was sure. She got up from her seat in the canoe, found a path across the stones to the shore and said, "*M'bloloani*" as casually as though she and the hostile-looking Fans said "Good day" to each other regularly. In Fan country, you were supposed to wait for your host to greet you, but sometimes rules of etiquette were better ignored, Mary felt.

She received several grunts in answer but the grunts were hardly cordial. A moment or so later a middle-aged man, with a twist of dirty cloth around his middle and a bunch of leopard and wildcat tails dangling from his shoulder, came through the crowd.

Pagan yelped, and ran toward him. He held his hands just off from touching the Fan's shoulder, in proper Fan greeting, and said, "Don't you know me, my beloved Kiva? Don't you remember your old friend?"

Kiva grunted sudden recognition and after an instant's hesitation returned Pagan's greeting warmly.

Mary saw Grey Shirt's hand relax above his gun and she slowly let out her own breath. These Fans were the wildest, wickedest-looking human beings she had ever seen. The minutes she had just lived through were the longest minutes she could remember experiencing.

Grey Shirt, too, found a friend among the Fans, and both he and Pagan brought their friends to Mary to be introduced. The shouting and talking began again and then Pagan, Grey Shirt, and Mary were swept up the steep path amid deafening clamor, to the village, leaving the others to guard the canoe. The noise grew worse when they started down the main street of the village, because every time a child saw Mary's white face, it went screaming into the nearest hut from terror.

The town was very dirty. Remains of a crocodile and piles of fish offal and decomposed elephant all combined to make a smell that was almost unbearable. Mary's nostrils quivered and she had a desperate feeling that she might be sick right in front of the village palaver house. She managed to avoid this by keeping her breathing shallow. It was absolutely necessary for her to remain in control of both body and spirit if she were to do business with these Fans.

"Tell them that we want to stay here tonight and that we want to hire three carriers for tomorrow to go with us to the Rembwé," she instructed Grey Shirt.

It took an hour and three quarters for this to be explained, argued, and re-explained. The air was suffocating even outdoors but when Mary was finally shown to her quarters for the night, she found that things could be worse. The bed in her hut was a rough bench of wood covered with a few filthy covers and offering a wooden pillow. From the bamboo roof hung a long stick with hooks on it. On the hooks were fetish charms, an ornament of wildcat and leopard tails tied to a square leopard skin. In the center of the skin was a little mirror and around the mirror were dozens of shirt buttons carefully sewed on. The tails had three little brass bells hung between them, to scare away snakes in the forest. There must be gorillas around, too, Mary decided, because she had noticed one of the old lady Fans wearing a necklace of sixteen gorilla teeth.

After inspecting the hut, Mary went back to the canoe with Grey Shirt and Pagan. The crew brought the canoe around to the main beach of the village. Kiva, who came down to guide his friends, informed Mary that only one other white person, a Frenchman, had ever come to their village before.

The trade box was carried to Mary's hut and she began the palaver, with Grey Shirt's help. At first her offers of pay for carriers were received with contempt, as was the custom. One man pretended to catch her words in his hand and throw them on the ground. But Mary had learned much about native trade. She shrugged her shoulders and looked out at the crowd with her arms folded and her head scornful.

A woman came up carrying smashed snail on a banana leaf. It was about the least appetizing trade item Mary had ever seen, but she gave the woman some fishhooks for it, to start things. The lady Fan promptly put the hooks into her mouth for safekeeping and went off. Other women, eager for similar treasures, crowded up, offering pineapples and other things but Mary, afraid she might run out of fishhooks, soon shut off this trade. She left Grey Shirt to carry on the palaver for the men she wished to hire, and went inside the hut to drink the tea Ngouta brought her. The only door was a hole in the hut and this hole was filled with staring faces as she ate some smoked fish and pineapple and drank her tea.

When she had finished her supper, she went outdoors again to take Grey Shirt's and Pagan's place while they had their chop.

"Sah no good as Ajumba," Grey Shirt informed her bluntly. "Sah make big big price. Too much no good for Fans." In other words, she had offered too high a salary to the carriers and that was causing some of the delay. If she raised the price any more, the palaver would take too long.

"How long does a palaver usually take around here?" Mary asked.

"Small price palaver maybe three weeks," said Pagan. "Big price palaver, no man know."

Three weeks! Mary looked back at the dirty little hut and shuddered. "My price is for a start tomorrow," she said firmly. "After tomorrow I have no price; I just go away. Tell them to put that in their pipes and smoke it."

This last bit of breeziness was lost on her interpreters but they somehow managed to make it clear to the Fans that this white trader, woman or not, meant what she said. Within an hour, the three richest men in the village had hired themselves out as carriers. Kiva was one of them. The other two were named Fika and Wiki. They said they knew the way as far as a Fan town called Efoua, where neither white man nor black trader had yet been. Beyond Efoua they did not know the territory but there had to be a path from Efoua to the Rembwé, they said, because the people of Efoua took their trade to the trading post on that river. The Fans agreed to go all the way to the Rembwé provided

Mary would guarantee their safety if they "found war" along the way.

Mary promised grandly, although she had not the slightest idea how she was to provide said safety. She told them they would be paid off at Hatton and Cookson's sub-factory on the Rembwé.

"Fans say they have looked your mouth and found it sweet," Grey Shirt reported when all this was talked over. This was local language for saying that the Fans liked Mary and her offers. "Palaver done set."

It was eleven thirty by the time Mary had unpacked her bottles of fishes to equalize the loads among the men and the rearranged loads had been tied up with bush rope. She stretched out, still dressed, on the wooden bed. They were to start before dawn.

Sleep was slow in coming. After scratching for an hour at various insect bites, Mary got up and slid aside the bark door to the hut. Pagan was asleep across the doorstep, under mosquito netting, as a guard. She stepped over him without waking him from his muttering sleep.

The town was quiet now. She walked down to the beach, took a paddle from a bunch thrust into the sand, slid off a small Fan canoe, and paddled out onto Lake N'covi.

The night was lovely and quiet, with no light except what came from the brilliant stars. An immense planet shone in the purple sky, making a yellow-white trail across the water. Here and there the stillness was broken by large fish leaping up out of the water, their silver-white bodies flashing like sabres. One lonely bird made a long, low boom-booming sound.

She steered across to the opposite shore. Seeing a large number of glowworms, she drove the canoe onto a bank of hippo grass, moored it and climbed out to obtain the worms for her collection. She was bending over, picking up the worms, when she felt the ground quiver and heard a strange sound which was a cross between a sigh and a groan. She looked around to see a herd of hippos looming out of the starlit darkness, making their way down a hippo walk to the water. The path seemed only inches away. Mary eyed the distance to her canoe, praying that the hippos would not see her or smell her presence.

She tiptoed backward, unable to make herself turn her back on the huge beasts, imagining that the instant she did, one would come lumbering after her. It had been reckless of her to stop right by their feeding grounds. She lost her footing on the slippery grass and the jarring noise as she caught her balance sounded like thunder in the silence. There was an answering bellow from one of the hippos and she stood rigid, seeing a big, clay-colored head turned toward her. White hunters put a mixture of oil and soot on their faces when they were after hippos; hippos had a quick eye for anything white. Fortunately, her dress was black.

She reached the canoe, clinging to her collection of glow-worms and trying to hold her skirts from swishing against the grass. As she got into the canoe, she heard the hippos splashing in the water. Gripping her paddle, she moved the canoe out from shore as noiselessly as possible and when she felt safe she stopped to look back.

The hippos seemed to have forgotten her. Several had found a spot of shallow water and stood there buried to their noses in the lake. Others, nibbling at the grass, chewed leisurely. Their tusklike teeth, the whitest of all ivory, made splashes of light in the night. At the edge of the herd one hippo mother stood with a baby hippo like a little fat hill on her back. The baby was making soft, happy grunts very much like those of a pig.

Mary left the glossy-backed herd to its banquet and bath and paddled on across the lake. Near the island, but at the opposite end from the Fan village, she came across a small, rocky bay with a patch of sand at the water's edge. This was not a hippo pool since there was no grass near, but it would make a wonderful swimming hole for her. After the lice and dirt in the Fan hut, a bath in this clear water seemed especially tempting.

Looking around to be sure that there were no Fans to spy on her, she stripped off her clothes and plunged into the star-spattered water. The wide sash she had left on shore would have to be her towel, she decided, as she splashed water over her face and arms and body.

When she dried herself and dressed again, dawn was almost at hand. She barely got back to the hut in time to pretend to be asleep when her crew called her.

The canoe party took off again at five thirty and followed a channel leading out of Lake N'covi at its northeast end. Mary and her enlarged crew followed this into another, smaller lake, and then pursued another channel as far as a canoe could take them.

Whatever Mary's opinion of the Fans had been before she started overland from Lake N'covi to the Rembwé River, her admiration for the three she had hired at the village of M'fetta grew daily. At the last minute a fourth Fan, whom she nicknamed The Duke because of his lordly manner, had come along uninvited and without pay. All four of the Fans were at home in the wild forest, walking over fallen trees and rocks with an easy grace. The Ajumbas, Ngouta, and the Igalwas were left far behind. Fortunately, the Fans had appetites as strong as their muscles. Every two hours they sat down, ate heartily and smoked a pipeful of tobacco. This gave Mary and the others in the party a chance to catch up. The Ajumba and Ngouta rested with the Fans. Mary, too, sat down for a few minutes during each halt, and then went on alone to explore and hunt for beetles.

She was ahead of everyone the afternoon of the first day of the land trek, on a path leading down into a ravine. Looking ahead, she saw a herd of five elephants wading and rolling in the mud. Luckily, she was downwind of them, or they might have charged her. Dodging behind a tree, she dropped to the ground, intending to wait there for someone else to show up.

She lay still for a few minutes but her curiosity soon got the better of her discretion. She began to creep toward the elephants, going cautiously from tree to tree. The elephants paid no attention. She came so close she could have hit one with a stone had she wished to, as they stamped their big feet and wallowed in the mud, scattering it with such force that it spattered her. There was a lot of ivory there, she noted with a trader's eye. Her men would covet those tusks. One of the beasts must have forty pounds of tusk on him, but he could keep it as far as she was concerned.

The animals were wonderful to watch. Some of them lay like pigs in the deepest mud, and some drew up trunkfuls of water and sprayed it over themselves and their friends. When they grew tired of their activities they strolled away. Stopping to rub their hides against a tree, they lumbered along Indian file, breaking off a few branches along the way, and disappeared into the bush.

The show over, Mary turned around to see where her men were and tripped over Kiva, who had been watching the elephants as quietly as she had. His eyes were gleaming and Mary asked if he wanted to go on an elephant hunt.

Kiva shook his head. "No go for hunt now. No got powder much. Save powder for war." She nodded, feeling relieved for the safety of the elephants in spite of his ominous forecast.

The other men arrived and began to wade through the elephant bath. Mary, following their lead, found it very rough going—like a nightmare exaggeration of a ploughed field. The elephant prints were about the size of a chair bottom and were filled with water and slippery. She fell so many times that she lost count but the men fared no better. She turned once to see Grey Shirt standing on one leg, his other one waving wildly in the air. Even the sure-footed Fan, Wiki, was knocked over when the man in front of him spun around and put his arms accidentally around Wiki's waist. Both hit the mud.

When they emerged from the wallow, Mary became aware of a fearful pricking in her arm. Rolling back her sleeve, she found an elephant tick poking its head into her flesh. An investigation of other pricks turned up three more of the insects, all of them so happy in their new homes that they had to be pried loose.

The other members of the party were busy picking similar ticks from their stomachs, arms, and legs. Watching their contortions and listening to their groans, Mary re-marked, "Elephant make too much dash one time."

It took a minute or two for her humor to be appreciated, even with the interpreter's help, but when the Fans realized that she meant the ticks were a present from the elephants, they laughed uproariously, hitting themselves and each other in their delight.

CHAPTER ELEVEN

THICK, WAXY FLOWERS OF ORANGE AND CRIMSON CARPETED the ground of the gloomy forest clearing where the travelers stopped for lunch.

The Duke, Mary's uninvited guest from M'fetta, as usual seated himself beside her and the tobacco tin. When he had filled his pipe, he asked Mary for a match.

She gave him one but curiosity prompted her to ask what he would do if she ran out of matches, since the natives carried none.

He smiled. From his loin cloth he produced a bush cow's horn on which was tied a wooden lid. This container held a flint and steel and The Duke demonstrated how simply he could produce his own light. Mary, who had so far despised The Duke, promptly revised her estimate. No wonder the other Fans treated him with respect. It was shrewd to make use of other people's possesssions and save your own for emergencies.

Mary had reason later that day to change her opinion of The Duke still another time when they came upon a snake about three and a half feet long and as thick as a human thigh, hanging from a branch over the path. Ngouta, who saw it first, jumped backward, shaking. The snake, called *Ompenle* by the Igalwas, was handsome, Mary thought, in its velvety new skin patterned in red-brown and yellow. The Ogowé natives hated and feared it, but not The Duke.

He stepped past Ngouta, flattened the head of the snake against the tree trunk with his gun butt, and then folded the creature up and stuffed all he could get of it into his bag. The rest of the snake dangled until suppertime, when the Fans and Mary cooked it for their evening meal, the other Africans looking on in disgust. Afterward, Mary noted in her notebook that a good snake, properly cooked, was one of the best meats she had eaten in Africa. She never let herself be squeamish about food, and this self-discipline helped to keep her alive all during her explorations and in the periodic bouts with malaria all white people in Africa experienced.

Wiki's pursuit of bush rope, a hobby with him, sometimes took him off on jaunts into the forest while the rest of the party were eating or smoking. He came back one day to their stopping place and asked Mary to come with him, very quietly, to see something. "Not far," he said, when she hesitated.

They were on the edge of a plantation near Egaja, a town that was supposed to be full of dangerous savages. Mary gave a few fearful glances to either side as she wormed her way between the bushes to follow Wiki.

They had gone about fifty yards when Wiki suddenly dropped flat, motioning Mary to look past him. About thirty yards away was a family of gorillas busily pulling down bananas—Papa, Elder Son, and three ladies, Mary noted. One of the females had a baby clinging to her back. The biggest male was crouching, his long arms hanging by his sides and the backs of his hands on the ground. The oldest female was tearing a pineapple to pieces and eating it.

On other occasions, Mary had heard gorillas roar with rage but now they were whinnying and chattering. The two largest were over six feet tall and the others not much smaller.

She put her hand over Wiki's gun to keep him from shooting them. He, in turn, thinking she wanted the gun to shoot, herself, gripped her wrist to prevent it. They stood a few seconds like that, then Wiki began to make a peculiar noise. Alarmed, Mary looked to see what was wrong with him. His face was twisted into a horrible mask and he was clutching his throat as though he were choking. His head rolled back and forth so hard she thought it might come off entirely. Suddenly he buried his face in some leaves at the foot of the tree and sneezed!

The gorillas all let go of whatever they were holding and stood up on their back legs. A sound somewhere between a bark and a howl came from one of them and then everyone except the old male took off into the bush. Papa Gorilla rose to his full height—he seemed ten feet tall at that minute, to Mary—and looked straight at her and Wiki.

She held her breath but Wiki, poor man, could not hold his. He was off on a sneezing fit. The gorilla must have decided Wiki was some new and possibly dangerous jungle animal, because he suddenly took off after his family, swinging from bough to bough, his long, hairy arms working swiftly.

"Man made a mistake when he had his arms shortened," Mary murmured as she and Wiki went back to join their companions.

"Sah?"

"Oh, never mind." The natives had a lively sense of humor but there were times when it was impossible to communicate across the language barrier.

As the expedition started to march again toward the town

of Efoua, the goal for the night, Mary brought them to a halt.

"Why not stay for bush?" she asked, remembering the lice-infested Fan hut in the village of M'fetta. She went on to argue that Efoua might be an unfriendly place, and they might find themselves simmering in a cooking pot if they went there. The Igalwa interpreter, Ngouta, agreed with her. He, too, considered sleeping in the forest a better plan.

Wiki, who obviously considered Ngouta a weakling, said not to worry. He had friends at Efoua. Besides, it was dangerous in this forest. He showed Mary trees with scratches which, he said gravely, could only have been made by leopards. It was better to go on as fast as possible.

Because Mary's legs grew stiff if she stopped walking very long, she was usually ahead of the others. About five o'clock she came to a path which, the guides had told her, was the one to follow. It was not a very clear path but she followed it with her eye as far as she could. Looking around, however, she thought she saw where it reappeared on the other side of a clump of underbrush, so she went in that direction. The next thing she knew she was lying on a small forest of spikes at the bottom of a bag-shaped game pit some fifteen feet below ground level.

The sky seemed suddenly a remote blue dot rimmed by the shaggy edges of the pit. Worst of all, she had landed on at least nine of the wicked spears and her weight was pressing her down against their points. Thankful for her thick shirts, she tried shakily to tuck a few more feet of cloth under her. She could never climb out of the pit alone, which meant she might be there some time.

She struggled to think of a native equivalent to the word "Help!" but her mind felt frozen. She settled for a good, old-fashioned scream, praying that some of her crew were close enough to hear.

The Duke arrived first, peering down at her.

"Get a bush rope and haul me out of here," Mary ordered.

The Duke grunted, scratched himself, and then sat down on a log, presumably to think.

The next arrival was The Passenger. He also looked down into the yellow, sand-clay lined trap and inquired, "You kill?"

"Half killed. Get a rope and haul me out."

"No fit," said The Passenger, and joined The Duke on his log.

Passenger was plenty fit when it came to eating, Mary said to herself, entertaining murderous thoughts of both men. If either of them had been resting on spikes which were ready to impale them at the slightest move, there would have been some loud howling! Well, she could howl, too. She yelled once more.

With relief, she heard the voices of Kiva and Wiki and a moment later saw their faces above her. Wiki promptly went off to hunt up the required bush rope, telling her to "Wait, sah." Mary wondered what else there was for her to do.

The minutes crawled by. After what seemed an eternity, Wiki returned, explaining that he had to hunt long and hard to find the proper strength of rope.

She was soon hauled out. Aside from a few rips in her dress and a peppering of small bruises she seemed to be in one piece, but the looks she gave The Duke and The Passenger were not very friendly.

Later, Silence also disappeared into a game pit, but not having a skirt or much else between his flesh and the spikes, he was more painfully wounded. Mary and his fellow-travelers applied cool green leaves to his wounds, and they went on, walking closer together now and inspecting the path ahead with care.

At Efoua, Mary conducted the usual trade palaver with the chiefs of the village and one of them made her his guest in an anything-but-snug hut. The structure did have two rooms, however, which meant that the men in her crew could use one and she the other.

While she waited for Ngouta to bring food and tea to her, she sat outside on a mushroom-shaped stool in the cool evening air. The chiefs settled down around her to ask why she had come. She told them she was going to the factory on the Rembwé. She did some trading, buying twenty-five balls of rubber which she didn't want or need, and some elephant-hair necklaces from a chief's wife. For this she traded her own red silk neck scarf and a few other items of apparel. Trade was shut off for the night when one of the chiefs tried to sell her an old, rusty razor wrapped in a bundle of bark cloth. She refused the bargain but gave him a belt to keep the peace, and went to bed.

It took a long time for the village to quiet down. The arrival of this peculiar white person was very exciting. Mary had just dozed off for the second time when she was awakened by a foul odor. Picking up a smoldering bush light from the floor, she tracked the smell to some bags hanging from the roof poles. She untied one and shook out its contents into her bonnet. The bag contained a human hand, three big toes, four eyes, and two ears.

Mary put them all quickly back into the bag and hung it up where she had found it. Sleep or no sleep, she would investigate no further. She realized, from information that Wiki and Kiva had given her, that such grizzly mementos of Fan victims often became fetish objects. The next time she was offered hospitality by a cannibal, she decided, she would take a tour of her quarters with her nose before she accepted.

To get the terrifying smell out of her nostrils, Mary went to the door of the hut for some breaths of air. There were no mosquitoes in Efoua and the night was beautiful. The town, surrounded by the black forest, looked wild in the starlight, its two rows of bark huts set off from the wilderness by a guardhouse at each end. The guards seemed to be asleep beside their fires. Only the goats, brought inside the village at night to keep them from the leopards, were moving about. She took some deep breaths, and went back to bed.

After Efoua, the way to the Rembwé became mountainous. The travelers were now at the equator and the heat was intense. To add to their troubles, they had to crawl over monstrous trees that had been torn up by tornadoes and lay across the trail. Even the natives, whose naked toes gave them an advantage on the slippery tree trunks, often went crashing into a tangle of branches. Mary's boots with their smooth soles were an extra handicap. She had to be hauled out of one tangle. Later, one of the Fans, Fika, went down with a heavy load on his back and it took a half hour for the other men and Mary, all hauling on the rope, to rescue him.

The land grew more difficult, seeming deliberately hostile as mountains alternated with swamps and bogs. No sooner would the party toil up one steep slope and down again than a swamp would appear at the bottom of the ravine. And each swamp was associated with a river. In the wet season, Mary realized, the trip would have been completely impossible. As it was, the sun had baked the crust on the larger swamps so that most were strong enough to support a human being if he moved swiftly. Mary set a fast pace across the treacherous crust, and the Fans imitated her. The others searched for safe places to step, and as a result they sank through the surface with a loud glug at times. The fat Pagan had the hardest time. Once he and The Passenger plunged through the surface together and Mary and the others had to slash off tree boughs and gather handfuls of hard leaves to make a kind of raft around the slime-covered pair until the indispensable bush rope could be brought to haul them to firmer ground.

The most beautiful swamps were the hardest to cross. The *shenja* plants that covered the sides of the ravines sparkled with green and gold, and the dark green leaves and red berries borne on tall, graceful stems at first excited Mary's admiration, but her appreciation faded when she tried to walk through the plants. The handsome stems were as strong as a double-stranded wire, and the lovely leaves, when they fell to the ground, were as slippery as soap.

The travelers were now trying to find a town called Egaja and a party of four young African rubber collectors showed them the best way to go in return for a gift of tobacco. The tired safari forded a deep, swift river, went through another forest, and continued downhill. Mary was just beginning to recover her breath from this trek when she saw, at the bottom of the hill, another steep ravine.

Could she, she asked herself, feeling close to complete exhaustion, wade through still one more swamp? She looked about at her crew. They were all waiting for her to take the next step. The Fans clearly accepted her as their leader and the boss of the expedition. Their only experience with white men had been with those who had had the courage to penetrate just such places as these, men who did not ask to be carried in a hammock or wheeled in a cart. She could not let those early, brave white missionaries and explorers down. And, although her Fan companions had earned her admiration and considerable trust so far, it would not be wise to betray weakness in front of them.

Wiki, who had been in front of Mary, turned to say something. Not fully grasping what it was, Mary stepped around him and looked ahead. Across the swamp lay a monster tree, bridging the ravine. She glanced from the tree to a river fifteen feet below, rushing over rocks and debris. Her second look at the natural bridge was not as encouraging as the first. The barkless trunk shone bare and round and exceedingly slippery. One misstep and the rocks below would finish her. Her legs shook with fatigue and her boots were sopping, their soles greasy with mud.

Boldly she demanded, "Who wants to go first?" and heard Ngouta repeat her question in Fan.

The Fans gabbled a second or two to each other and then waded into the river, paying no attention to the tree bridge. Swimming and wading by turns, they reached the other side of the ravine. Everyone else except Mary and Pagan decided the water was fine, too, and with the help of the Fans, were brought up on the other side.

"You next," Mary said to Pagan as calmly as though her breath were not stuck in her throat. If she tried to swim, she would probably drown, in her present exhausted condition. She played for time to decide just how she was to get across.

Pagan chose the bridge. He went gingerly about three yards out on the tree, slipped, and caught himself on a knob of the trunk. This settled the matter for him. He came back to where Mary stood, mumbled something sheepishly, and waded into the water as the others had done.

Mary shut her eyes, counted to ten, opened them again and marched out onto the tree trunk. Now of all times, Africa had its chance to kill her, if that was what it wanted. With a sense of defiance, she walked swiftly on, not looking down. To her amazement she reached the other side safely.

The men started to tease Pagan, then, because the "sah" had crossed on the tree and he had fallen off.

"Fans say they go for water to wash feet," Ngouta interpreted to Mary with a broad grin. "Fans say they not afraid of tree, only like clean feet."

It was a very big joke, apparently, to everyone except Pagan. Under the laughter, Mary detected a grimmer note and caught some sullen looks. Whether it was the teasing of Pagan that started the bad feeling among the men, or something else, a change took place in the mood of her crew, a change that could mean trouble for her.

Her apprehension increased as the day went on. The Fans wanted to stop and go hunting. She had to explain that she did not have enough money with her to stop then but that she hoped to come back another year and then she would be delighted to join them on a hunt. Glancing at their scowling faces and hearing their mutters, she had moments when she doubted that she would be alive to go hunting the next year. She urged them determinedly on to the village of Egaja.

Pondering the Fans' urge to hunt, she remembered an experience she had had one afternoon when she was beetle hunting. She had gone off by herself along a path in the forest. The path opened up into a small clearing and there she suddenly came face to face with seven hooded men. On the hoods, and on the cloaklike garments they also wore, were beads and cloth and shells and other unidentifiable decorations. Even before coming to Africa, Mary had heard of the terrible Leopard Society and other secret and dangerous groups in the bush, and her heart went into her mouth. It was certain death for any outsider to witness secret ceremonies, she had been told.

Mary had tried to slip away silently, but running footsteps told her that she might as well turn around and face whatever danger was in store for her. The hooded man who had pursued her did not speak, but indicated with his hands that she was to follow him. There seemed to be nothing to do except obey. When they reached the six other members of the group, Mary was given some sort of salute, but not knowing just what it meant she felt no reassurance. Still no one said anything, unless the occasional howl one or the other gave out could be called a word.

The hooded men traveled for about a mile, Mary with them, until they came to another clearing in the woods. There they all sat down nearly motionless, except Mary, whose nerves by that time were in a very jumpy state. She leaned against a tree.

Nothing happened for about twenty minutes—twenty minutes which seemed twenty years to Mary—and then monkeys began to appear. In pairs, and sometimes in larger groups, holding each other by the hand, the curious animals came closer and closer to the hooded men. When they were close enough, the men brought arrows from under their cloaks and shot them. Five of the monkeys were killed before the rest came to their senses and ran away from danger.

Mary realized then that she had not been kidnapped by

any secret society of African terrorists. She was only on a monkey hunt. The natives, knowing how curious monkeys are, dressed themselves up in fantastic costumes to attract the animals' attention and draw them close enough to be killed. The hooded men explained to Mary that since she was the queerest-looking person they had ever seen, in her long skirts and bonnet and with her umbrella and collecting equipment, they were sure to catch some monkeys if she were with them.

No one offered to share the hunting spoils with her and Mary was just as glad. She had not been hungry enough to eat a monkey just then, and she disliked killing things or seeing them killed, except in self-defense or for food.

The time might come any minute, she told herself now as she and her crew trudged wearily on toward their destination, when she might be very happy to eat monkey. She had eaten nearly every other kind of meat Africa had to offer.

Egaja was considered an evil town even among the Fan tribes, but there was no other place to stay. The chief of Egaja was fishing downriver when Mary arrived but was promptly sent for by his fellow tribesmen. Meanwhile, Mary was shown to a large hut of four rooms. By the time her baggage and that of her crew was put inside, the chief had arrived and she went outside to meet him.

A powerful and intelligent-looking man, he wore a man's double-breasted black coat which reached his knees, a bright blue felt sombrero and a loin cloth of some checked material. Very courteous, he ordered stools brought for himself and Mary and also a whisk of leaves to keep off the sandflies. Pagan came to act as interpreter between Mary and her host.

Mary asked Pagan to give the chief her compliments and then added, "Tell him, however, that we have heard this town is thief-town."

"Better not, sah!" Pagan was flabbergasted.

"Go on," Mary said firmly.

Pagan did as he was told, keeping a safe distance from the chief as he spoke.

The chief burst into shocked protests. "Thief-town! Egaja town be most honorable town," Pagan translated. "Be example to all towns hereabouts. Chief say it be terrible that sah hear such bad tings about his town. Chief be most sad."

Mary could see that the chief was indeed sad. She could hardly keep back a smile at his attempts to indicate the depth of his sorrow and shock. Through Pagan she told him that she would not believe the bad things unless bad things happened while she and her men were there. The subject was changed and she began to ask the chief questions about the religion of his tribe and other matters that interested her. They were soon talking almost without Pagan's help, like old friends.

After Mary had something to eat, the chief brought his old mother to her to see if the white "sah" could do something for the old lady's infected hand. Some river creature, probably a crocodile, had wounded the hand and an abscess had formed. Mary opened the abscess, washed it out, and made a poultice of fresh banana leaves and boiling water. During the process the patient, her pain greatly lessened, fell asleep. Mary roused her enough to give her some pills and then had her carried to her own home.

This "miracle" brought a flood of other patients to her for treatment, including the chief himself, who wanted some of the same pills she had given his mother. Mary, her stomach churning at the sight of some of the dreadful ulcers and abscesses among her visitors, gave out advice and help as best she could. One man had *filaria*, small worms, in the white of one eye. These were traveling across his nose into the other eye, under the skin, looking like a bridge.

Mary's new friend, the chief of Egaja, watched all the treatments and then went for bark cloth to put over Mary's plank bed. She thanked him with some gifts of knives and tobacco and wearily bade the grateful man good night.

At 1:45 in the morning, sleep was punctured by a frantic female scream. Mary, jolted awake, felt compelled to go out and investigate. She had her own suspicions about the cause of the trouble and was entirely right. One of her crew of Fans had tried to steal something. She paid damages, gave a lecture to the guilty man, and went back to bed.

At four o'clock she was wakened once more. This time there seemed to be many screams and shouts and yells, even drum-beating. With such a din, there could be a war on, Mary thought, her heart thumping.

"Go see what for," she called out to the Ajumbas who were sleeping in the next room.

"No go Fan town now," Grey Shirt answered nervously after a few minutes of silence. "Big big danger. Ajumba man get killed."

"Maybe Kiva killed now," Mary called back worriedly. The Fan members of her party were not sleeping in her hut. As tribal relatives of the Egaja people, they had secured their own sleeping quarters elsewhere in the village. She was sure she had heard Kiva's voice in the babel outdoors, high in pitch as it was when he was arguing.

If the Ajumbas would not go out, she would have to. After all, she had promised Kiva and the other Fans "safety" if anyone made war on them. Putting on her boots, the only part of her costume she had removed when she went to bed, she stepped over the silent Ajumbas and went out into the street.

Kiva was tied to a tree not very far from Mary's hut, talking as fast as he could talk, his voice shrill. In front of him was an Egaja Fan brandishing a knife inches from Kiva's throat.

"What's the trouble?" Mary asked in the best Fan language she could muster. Ngouta, her interpreter, was huddled with his Ajumba friends in her hut.

"Kiva man no good," the Egaja man said sullenly, keeping his knife pointed at his victim. "He not bring coat. He tief." He took a step nearer Kiva, who tried to wriggle out of his bonds but failed to budge them.

Coat! What kind of coat was Kiva supposed to have brought? Mary wondered. She saw that she would have to insist on an interpreter. She went and woke Ngouta, then came back and learned the whole story. It seemed that some time ago Kiva had promised the Egaja Fan a beautiful coat in return for a tooth of elephant ivory. The Egaja said he had stopped by Kiva's village of M'fetta many times to get the coat but Kiva was never at home. Furthermore, he claimed, one of Kiva's wives stole a yellow dog of great value from his canoe while he was at M'fetta.

Mary asked sternly if this was true.

Kiva looked at the ground, muttering something which, translated, meant that women were women. Ngouta told Mary that the argument had been going on so long that the Egaja now were bringing up dozens of crimes Kiva had committed in the past, for which he ought to be killed, in their opinion. Mary had to strain to hear what her interpreter said, because the Fans on both sides of the argument were talking and yelling so loudly.

She held up her hand and shouted "*Azuna!*" Her knife

lay back in the hut so she could not have cut Kiva's bonds
if she had dared to. She had no gun, while each one of the
men who faced Kiva with such anger kept a hand close to
his. The case would have to be decided according to local
law and she would have to preside over the court, if she
and her men were to get out of the situation alive. The
African people had a great respect for their tribal laws.

She asked the other Fans in her own party what they
thought of the justice of the charges against Kiva. Their
attitude was that the things the Egaja men were talking of
were not true—and, anyway, they had happened too long
ago. By this time, the chief whose mother Mary had treated
the night before had got out of his bed and joined them.
With his help Mary settled the case by paying, out of the
stores in her trade box, for the coat Kiva had not provided.
She told the Egaja men she would take the cost of the goods
from Kiva's pay when they reached the factory on the
Rembwé. She disliked parting with so much of her merchandise, since there was still a long distance to travel before
they reached the Rembwé, but it seemed to be the only
possible solution.

Perhaps now, she thought hopefully, as she went to bed
again, life would be more peaceful. But the next day, her
crew quarreled all during the preparations for going on
with their journey. Mary ignored them. She went with the
chief to look at his mother's hand once more, and left instructions about keeping the wound clean. The old woman,
her face solemn with gratitude, took Mary's hands into
her own, turned the palms upward, and blew into them.

"She blows you a blessing," Ngouta explained.

The chief presented Mary with some charms "to keep
her foot in path" to show his own gratitude. Escorting
her to the edge of the village, he asked if she still thought

Egaja was a thief-town, something he had apparently been brooding about.

"Egaja-town certainly not thief-town," Mary declared, shaking the chief's hand. She went on to say that she would tell anyone she met that this was the truth—she had not lost a single thing while she was there.

. . . Except, she added to herself, about seven hours of sleep.

❧ CHAPTER TWELVE

MARY'S EXPEDITION MOVED ON INTO THE GLOOM OF THE Great Forest. The trees seemed to stretch endlessly above and around them. She found herself walking dreamily, mesmerized by the silence and the lack of sky. She seemed to have walked into a never-never land where the rest of her life would be spent taking one step after another in this shadowy world, to bed down night after night in some noisy savage community.

Her companions seemed to like the forest. Their mood had brightened and they went yelling and singing up hill and down. Whatever had caused their ugly, earlier mood, it had apparently vanished. Mary wondered if she would ever understand these dark-skinned friends of hers. Perhaps no white wanderer, English or French or German, ever could. She was glad, however, of the change in their mood.

Walking along one day in one of those abstracted and thoughtful moods, Mary fell into a water-filled gully. The water, though tepid, shocked her out of her absent-mindedness. As she hauled herself up the steep banks, panting against the weight of her drenched clothing, she realized suddenly that it had been some time since she had heard any voices or even the crackling of leaves and twigs. There was no need for concern, she told herself. She had wandered off like this before. Sooner or later, she and her men always found each other.

The day was intensely hot. She took off her cap, hoping that some stray breeze would come to stir her wet hair and dry the perspiration and water from her face but the air was too moist. She put the damp cap on again and listened. The woods were intensely silent; only the soft cries and murmurings of birds came to her ears. She would be happier, she thought, to hear the less musical voice of Pagan or Wiki or the others.

She wrung out her still-dripping skirt and went on climbing. Her efforts and the drumming heat made her tongue grow dry and her breath come in gasps. Scrabbling at the rocks on the steep slope, she had a sudden, painful remembrance of her mother's last weeks of life. Mama had fought for breath in almost this same way. Mary paused, catching her breath. She might be the pace-setter for her crew, but there was no need for such frantic haste just now.

But there was. The familiar taste of salt in her mouth, a taste she had experienced on other occasions of danger, told her so. She was lost. She could not even be sure that she was not climbing back up the same side of the gully she had been descending when she fell. She stopped a minute and looked around, trying to think, and then went on, hoping she was on the right path. Once she reached the top, she persuaded herself, she would see the figures of her companions straggling along below. Or, if not, a strong halloo would bring them to her.

Near the top of the slope she stopped again. The sky had grown wild-looking and a peculiar light swept across what had earlier been a hot, staring blue when she glimpsed it through a gap in the trees. She redoubled her efforts to reach the top, recognizing the signs of a tropical tornado. Then a giant wind struck at the tree tops, rocking the forest giants with its monstrous breath—rocking Mary, too, as she hung against the slope. Shrieking and howling like a pack of famished wolves, the wind leaped from tree to tree, ripping off huge branches and shaking the leafy tops like so many green mops.

Mary drew in her breath, looking upward in combined terror and admiring awe.

There was a tearing, grinding noise. A bush vine which had been straining to hold back a falling tree, split. With a mighty swoosh the forest giant topped sidewise, knocking down smaller trees in its fall. The wind from this crash washed against Mary's face and lifted the damp strands of her hair as she climbed on.

A second later, the rain came, pouring down in torrents as if the sky were a gigantic pail that had been tipped. Water streamed over Mary's face and hands in rivers that seemed almost like tributaries of the mighty Ogowé.

The top of the slope was not far now but she wondered if she was going to reach it. She opened her mouth to cry out but clamped it shut again. No one could hear her above the howl of the wind and the crescendos of rain.

The top was near now. Only one sullen boulder was in her way. She clambered over it and stood, shaking and suddenly chilled, on the crest of the slope, the wind and the rain wrapping her in their wild garments. She looked around, hoping for the sight of a dark, friendly figure, but she saw only the storm. The taste of salt in her throat grew sharper.

For a moment or two, she stood motionless, her thoughts churning. She would have to depend on her wits to get her out of this predicament. Addled wits, they were, too, to have brought her to this ferocious spot.

Soberly, she watched yet another big tree crash against its neighbors. Perhaps she had always been lost. Perhaps only a lost soul would have tackled the job she had tackled. This was not, after all, just some safe though dreary task left over from other people's lives, this challenging of a remote and uncharted world. This expedition, and the earlier ones she had undertaken, offered challenges that even strong, bold men did not care to tackle. And here she was, a foolish spinster in ragged, sodden skirts, dreaming that there was reason and purpose in being where she was.

She closed her eyes against the driving rain. There was a purpose! The rain pricked her mouth—and she was not sure but what there were tears mixed in. The immediate purpose was to survive, physically and spiritually, so that she could accomplish her larger purpose of contributing some small portion to human understanding. She had to see to it that the collections she had so carefully preserved were shepherded back to England, that the notes she had kept, writing them by bush light, moonlight, or with the aid of a candle, were made available to scholars interested in such things.

Through the blur of the rain she seemed to see her father's figure hunched over his beloved manuscripts and books. As if the wind drove suddenly through her, opening up new spaces in her heart and mind, she knew that she no longer cared only to finish her father's work; she wanted something more. A new world was coming into being, with new, living students, new workers in foreign fields. She wanted to help those men and women of the future, both white and black, to understand each other. The peoples of Africa, in Lambaréné or Gaboon, on the coast or in the interior, up and down the immense, sprawling landscape, seemed invisibly to surround her, their faces sometimes bewildered, sometimes hostile, but often friendly and hopeful.

Lost. The word drummed in her mind in tune with the rain. No traveler could be lost who found himself.

A noise she had not noticed before made her turn toward a clump of lower-growing trees. Less than a yard away stood a leopard! Crouched against the ground, his huge head reared back, his eyes closed, he made Mary's breath stick in her throat. His front paws were spread out before him, the talons hooked through the soil, his tail lashing slowly behind him. Lightning flashed and his eyes opened suddenly to glare around him at the wind-tossed trees.

She shrank back against the boulder she had so recently climbed. Those smouldering eyes had not seen her, she felt. The growls rumbling in his chest were at the storm, not her. If she stayed where she was, utterly still, he might not discover her. Frightened though she was, she was also much moved by the leopard's beauty. He seemed a god of the landscape, a lithe and flower-spotted creation meant to rule nature. Yet he cowered before the lightning. The shining eyes were polished with animal terror.

One great paw moved, the talons piercing the decayed vegetation near the boulder. Holding her breath, Mary moved cautiously backward. The wind had become a friend, blowing her scent away from the leopard.

Huddled against the rock, watching the lightning-riddled sky, she imagined that she could hear the leopard's breathing above the wind's roar. Who would have imagined that shy Mary Kingsley, poring over copies of *The English Mechanic* years ago, or chasing unruly gamecocks through a suburban garden, would ever be alone in a wind-tormented forest of French Africa, listening to the sigh and mutter of a leopard?

She waited ten minutes, fifteen, twenty. There was no sound now but the wail of the storm and the clashing of leaves and branches. She peered around the boulder, cautiously.

The leopard was gone. The spot where he had rested was empty. Mary stared at the trampled vegetation and the uprooted soil, half in relief and half with a peculiar sorrow. She would probably never again see a leopard in all his animal majesty so closely.

She might never see her good friends Wiki and Silence and the others again, either, she realized, if she did not do something besides huddle on this wet rock and admire leopards.

Stumbling through the diminishing rain, calling as loudly as she could, she heard, finally, an answering shout. A few minutes later, in a flash of lightning, she saw one of her Fans, his bare, wet legs gleaming, a few feet away. She felt like embracing him but she restrained herself. In her most authoritative voice she demanded, "Were you lost yourself all this long time?"

Africa gave Mary a second chance to see a leopard at close range when her expedition was spending a night in a native village farther along the way. Alone in the hut which her Fan friends had hired for her, Mary was half-asleep when a ferocious clamor broke out in the decrepit hut next to her own. This hut, she remembered, was a dog house. In it lived a half-breed boarhound, very savage. Judging by the noise, the dog was killing all the other dogs in the village, Mary thought angrily. Getting out of bed, she slipped her feet into her boots, grabbed up a couple of the one-legged stools the natives favored and rushed out into the moonlight.

The moonlight was fading but there was enough light to see a whirling jumble of animals about two yards from her door. "Stop!" she shouted, throwing a stool at the snarling jumble. The animals quieted for a second but then went into action again. Mary yelled again, this time in Fan. Taking more careful aim, she threw the second stool after the first.

The stool hit its target with a resounding smack. The fight broke up and the animals separated with retreating growls. Only then did Mary see that one of them was a leopard. He crouched, ready to spring, his huge, brilliant eyes flaming at her in the moonlight. Reaching inside the hut, she grabbed up a clay pot and flung it straight at the terrifying eyes, shouting "Go home, you fool!" She did not want him to attack her but neither did she want him to be shot. The clay utensil burst against the leopard's skull and he took off for the forest with great speed.

By that time a number of the villagers were also awake, although Mary noted with amusement that none of them came near as long as the noise kept up. Well, she told herself, I wouldn't have pitched in myself if I had known I was tackling a leopard.

Kiva and Wiki were the only men from her own party who showed up. "Dog hurt bad," Wiki said. "Go for dead one time, sah." He showed Mary a slit in the boarhound's shoulder.

"You hold the beast, Wiki, and I fix him," Mary ordered. She went back into her hut and got her medical supplies. When she came out again, several natives, including the man who owned the dog, had managed to corral the animal so that Mary could clean the wound. The dog snapped at her, his teeth grazing her hand, as she worked.

"The leopard might have been more grateful for my services," Mary said grimly. She could still visualize those wonderful eyes looking at her in the moonlight.

The Fans told her that leopards always came after dogs. "A long time ago," they said, "the leopard and the dog were great friends. The leopard went out to hunt food for her children one day and left her babies with the dog. The dog saw another dog and went off to play. While he was away, a snake came and killed the leopard's children. Ever since then, the leopard and the dog have been enemies."

The dog might be man's best friend, Mary reflected, but he was certainly not the leopard's. The native legend was one of many she collected from the different tribes she met.

The Hatton and Cookson's factory on the Rembwé was located at a village called Agonjo. There Mary settled accounts with the Fans who had guided her from Lake N'covi to the river. Also, because she had come to like and respect these African cannibals so much, she divided among them what was left of the trade goods she had carried on the journey. The Ajumbas—Grey Shirt, Singlet, Pagan, and Silence—were going back the way they had come and would be paid at Lambaréné, by their own request. Mary gave them an order for goods at the Lambaréné store.

Resting in the room she had been given at the Agonjo trading headquarters, Mary wrote in her travel diary, "The Fans are real men, full of fire, temper, intelligence and go." Putting the pen down for a moment, she stared at the words she had written. How was she ever going to be able to portray, on paper or any other way, what she had learned from and about these cannibal people? She had no education except what she had wrung for herself from books, so how could she hope to be a writer? Yet there was little good in her having learned anything unless she could somehow communicate it to the people at home—or to any country that had colonies in Africa. The minds of Europeans had somehow to be cleared of the notion that the African was half brute, half child. The Africans were men, especially the Fans—virile, intelligent, and courageous men. Given the right kind of help and understanding, they would one day make their own unique and valuable contributions to the art, the knowledge and the advancement of man. She thought over the long, difficult journey she and the Fans had shared with a feeling of wonder that it could have happened at all. But it had, and some day she would be back to visit the Fans again.

The trip down the Rembwé River to Gaboon and the sea was made with an entirely new crew, captained by a man named Obanjo who preferred to be called Captain Johnson. He was a huge man, only part African, dressed in a sombrero, undershirt, and conventional trousers. His canoe was of hard wood but its sail had known better days. An old bed sheet, it was patched with the same material as the captain's trousers were, and in some cases it was open to the wind. At one end of the canoe was a platform under which the luggage was stored, and Mary sat on top of this.

By now an expert steersman, Mary took over the steering at night to relieve Captain Johnson for sleep. She found it a profound pleasure, and wrote of it later: "Much as I have enjoyed life in Africa, I do not think I ever enjoyed it to the full as I did on those nights dropping down the Rembwé. The great, black, winding river with a pathway in its midst of frosted silver where the moonlight struck it: on each side the ink-black mangrove walls, and above them the band of star and moonlit heavens that the walls of mangrove allowed one to see. Forward rose the form of our sail, idealized from bedsheetdom to glory; and the little red glow of our cooking fire gave a single note of warm color to the cold light of the moon. . . . while I was steering along by the south bank, I found the mangrove wall thinner, and standing up, looked through the network of their roots and stems on to what seemed like plains, acres upon acres in extent, of polished silver—more specimens of those awful slime lagoons."

Sometimes, on those nights, Mary steered into tree shadows and for a moment or two scared herself by thinking she had landed on a mud bank.

She slept much of the daylight hours, when it was intensely hot, except when they stopped briefly at some village. At one of the villages, Captain Johnson had one of his numerous wives and also some goats; he stopped to drive some of the goats onto the boat so that he could sell them at Gaboon. She was watching the good captain trying to corral the animals when a well-educated, pleasant voice said in English, "Most diverting spectacle, madam, is it not?"

She turned, startled, and saw a man standing on the bank near where the canoe was beached. She described him as "what appeared to be an English gentleman who had . . . gone black all over and lost his trousers and been compelled to replace them with a highly ornamented tablecloth. The rest of his wardrobe was in exquisite condition, with the usual white jean coat, white shirt and collar, very neat tie, and felt hat . . ."

The two of them discussed Liverpool, London, and Paris, Mary feeling as if she must be dreaming the incident, because how could a native of this remote section know what he did about the world she had left behind her?

He told her that his name was Prince Makaga. Makaga, Mary knew, was the title of honor given to the bravest and best hunter in a tribe. When Captain Johnson returned and they were traveling downstream once more, she gestured back at the man on the bank. "Who is he?" she asked.

The Prince, Captain Johnson told her, had once been an agent for a European firm at Gaboon and while acting in that capacity had made several trips to Europe.

Remembering his references to well-known art galleries, Mary thought that he must have made excellent use of his time while he was in England. Once again she was filled with enthusiasm for the potentialities of the natives of Africa.

Later that same afternoon, Mary was lying on her platform, catching up on her sleep, when the cry of "Fans! The Fans!" went up.

She sat up and asked what was happening.

"The men say many Fans with knives and guns come down the riber fast fast. They are afraid," reported Captain Johnson. With his foot he prodded one of the men who had dropped to the bottom of the boat. "Get up!" he shouted.

It was no use. All of the other men had also dropped to the boat's bottom.

The captain shook a disgusted fist at them. He said to Mary, "You take rudder, sah. Go for middle of riber, keep sail full."

"But—"Mary began. Sitting up, steering, she would be a first class target. Still, someone had to do it and the captain was getting out his gun. She grabbed the helm and sent the canoe into the middle of the river, the breeze behind helping. The captain fastened the mainsail, got out some paddles and one old oar, forcing a couple of the men to use them, while he jumped onto the platform with his gun ready.

A Fan canoe shot into view and came within twenty yards. More canoes full of Fans appeared behind the first and Mary's crew once more dropped their paddles and hid.

Captain Johnson demanded to know from the Fans why they were chasing him.

A woman in the bow of the first canoe burst into sobs. "My son! My son!" she seemed to be wailing.

It turned out that one of the younger members of Captain Johnson's crew was the woman's runaway son. The Fans had come to make him return to his village, and in spite of his protests, he was handed over to them.

Mary's admiration for native Africans was not blind. She despised the crew of Captain Johnson's canoe but she liked the captain himself. He evidently returned her affection because, as they entered the Gaboon River and neared their destination, he tried to talk her into a trading voyage up a notoriously dangerous river, in Spanish territory. Mary was to buy goods at the town of Glass in Gaboon and the captain would take her goods to buy ivory in the interior.

"Where will my profit come from?" Mary asked.

He looked hurt and disappointed. "You say, see this country. Ah! I say you come with me. I show you plenty country, plenty men, elephants, leopards, gorillas. Oh! plenty ting. Then you ask, 'Where's my trade?'"

Mary was sorry to have seemed mercenary but she nevertheless turned the invitation down. She was afraid she would end up with another crew as bad as this one. Captain Johnson was brave—but what if he got shot in the wild country and she was left to nurse him as well as steer and manage an unmanageable canoe?

"I've seen all the elephants, gorillas and leopards I need to for a while," she told the disappointed captain.

They arrived at Glass in late August, 1895, and Mary spent some weeks in the Gaboon district. She was eager to talk to Dr. Nassau because of his fund of knowledge concerning fetish and the customs of the tribes around Gaboon. On her earlier visit, she had only skirted the edge of all she wanted to ask the good missionary.

While the two of them were talking at his house one evening, Dr. Nassau mentioned that there were lakes on the island of Corisco near Libreville. "The ladies of Corisco are the only people who are permitted to fish there and they fish only once a year. You might be able to get in on this year's expedition, though. My head boy, Eveke, is the son of the native missionary on the island, Mr. Ibea, and he can go with you. I'll let you have my boat, the *Lafayette*."

Mary accepted this offer promptly and with a crew headed by Eveke Ibea, the *Lafayette* left Libreville at eight in the morning. From the boat, Mary looked back at the town, thinking how pretty it was in the sunshine with its red roofs and white walls backed by dark green mango trees.

The sea was rough and the sun very hot. She dropped to the bottom of the boat, and bracing herself against her collecting box, took out her pen to make some entries in her journal. From where she sat she could see only the mainsail and the white crests of the waves racing by, but it was enough. Those sights, and the sound of the rustling sail and the swish of the waves were among life's pleasures to sea-loving Mary.

When the crew fell asleep, she got up and took the main sheet and tiller herself, despite the heat, only letting go when the boat neared the small bay where Eveke said they were to anchor.

On shore, Mary walked with mixed feelings across the wet, pink sand and the piles of seaweed. Corisco was almost out of tobacco because the sea had been too rough for the inhabitants to take canoes to the mainland, and the only people who came to greet her at first were the men who wanted tobacco. The sand was pretty but the seaweed caught at her ankles, and centipedes and sandflies were crawling over it.

At the mission house, however, Eveke's pretty mother and several daughters came to meet them. Mrs. Ibea said that her husband was away on an evangelizing trip for a few days but that Mary was very welcome and must accept her room while she stayed on the island. Her hostess also brought tea and alligator pears, which tasted delightful after the rough, hot sea voyage.

Getting fish, however, was not as easy as she had hoped. Eveke told her, the following day, that the ladies were not quite ready to go fishing. They were just finishing their planting on the farms before tornado time. "They can only catch fish in baskets," he explained. "The ladies say they will make the baskets soon." He smiled.

Mary understood the smile all too well. When a West African said "soon" he could mean days or weeks, even months. Time scarcely existed south of forty degrees latitude. She resigned herself to waiting on the island until the women were ready. Mrs. Ibea escorted her to the mission house and showed her to a room where she could wash and sleep.

While she waited, Mary explored the island. Three miles long and less than two miles wide, Corisco was a world in miniature. Miniature swamps led to miniature forests with small trees and plants. The villages, too, were small, each one having only a few houses.

She was resting on a low precipice overlooking the ocean when word came that the women of Corisco were ready to go fishing. Mary hurried to the mission house for her collecting equipment and joined the party.

They set off for the lakes by a path that went down a steep ravine, crossed a dry swamp, climbed a hill and then went across a small prairie and through woods to another prairie. On this second prairie the women set down their fishing baskets, opened their mouths wide, and began to howl.

"*On-gou-ta!*" they howled sadly but loudly. "*On-gou-ta!*"

Luckily, Mrs. Ibea had sent one of the mission school girls along with Mary as interpreter.

"What's the matter?" Mary asked her.

"Fish lady not all here. Ober fish lady come, den all ladies fish long time right."

Still bewildered, Mary decided that they were waiting for some special woman to go fishing with them. Probably her name was "On-gou-ta." Whoever or whatever On-gou-ta was, she did not show up after a half hour of howls. The women, unwilling to go on without her, lay down on the soft, golden-brown grass and fell asleep.

Mary looked up at the broiling sun and around at her sleeping companions, wondering what to do. Sleeping under such circumstances was not inviting. She put up her umbrella and sat down in its scant shade to study some beetles swarming over a nearby hillock.

Time passed. One hour. Two. The heat made Mary's own eyelids droop. She wished she knew when, if ever, her snoring companions were going to wake.

Then she became aware of a faint crackling sound from behind her. It grew louder and there seemed to be a noise like pistol shots behind it. She turned to see a fog of blue-brown smoke moving toward where they were resting.

Behind the smoke was a reddish glow. She leaped to her feet, her throat dry. The prairie was on fire!"

"Yayee!" she cried and shook the woman nearest to her. "Fire! Fire! Much hot! Get up!"

The sleeper grunted and kicked out at Mary, determined to go on sleeping. Mary gave her a prod in the ribs with her umbrella and she sat up abruptly. Mary pointed at the reddening smoke and the woman screamed.

In an instant, all the sleepers awoke. They jumped to their feet and ran from the advancing flames, heading for a forest, their bare feet smacking against the dry grass. Mary sprinted after them, her knees weak as she felt the fierce breath of the fire at her back.

The wind veered, fortunately, just after she and the women fishers reached the forest. From the trees, they watched the flames change direction and sweep past. Three of the women who had not moved quite fast enough had suffered minor burns. Not having her medical kit with her, Mary had no means of relieving their pain until, not long afterward, they reached a lake. There she persuaded the women to soothe themselves with the cool mud on the lake's edge; it might not heal but it stopped their moans of pain.

"We fish now plenty much," the mission school girl said. "No wait longer."

It's an ill fire that brings no good, Mary thought to herself as she and the women with their baskets headed for the lake.

The Corisco lakes were actually large pools encircled with rims of rock and forest. Several of the women, their wrap-around skirts caught and knotted above their knees, jumped from the rock rim into knee-deep black slime. Squealing and grunting, they made their way out to the deeper water in the middle of the pool while the rest of the party took their baskets and lined up at a spot where the mud ended and the clear water began.

Mary perched on a suitable rock to observe this new fishing technique. In the middle of the pond, the women were striking the water with sticks or their hands, obviously trying to drive the fish toward shore. The women at the water's edge were holding their baskets half in the water, the mouths of the baskets tipped to catch the onrush of fish. With a shout of triumph one of the women lifted a dripping fish-pot to display her squirming batch.

One of the women held a basket out to Mary, jabbering something and motioning toward the line-up. Mary accepted the proffered help eagerly. Rolling Charles' trouser cuffs up under her skirt, she removed her shoes and stockings, but she did not knot her skirts up between her legs as the other women had done. Some habits from her upbringing made such informality of dress impossible to her, no matter how practical it might be. Anyway, her skirts had been soaked so often in Africa, once more would make no difference. A little wetness was a small price to pay for a lesson in fish chasing.

By the end of the day, twelve bushels of fish lay gleaming in the women's baskets. Feeling as if she had discovered a fortune, Mary selected the rarest specimens from the catch for her collection. Some of them were very small and the women looked at her in astonishment. Who could feast on such morsels?

That night, the smell of cooking fish permeated the air all over Corisco. Mrs. Ibea told Mary that the annual fish chase was always celebrated with a huge fish feast. Afterward, the fishes that remained were smoked and kept as a delicacy until the next year's fishing day came around.

The return trip of the *Lafayette* from Corisco to Gaboon was a stormy one. The ship was forced onto a tongue of sand the first evening, and in order to get off again Mary had to use her umbrella to take soundings over the stern of the boat, as no sounding equipment was provided on the *Lafayette*. No lamps were provided, either, and the ship was tossing too much even for a fire to be lighted to boil tea. The sea washed over cargo and crew, and over a woman and her husband who had invited themselves along as unpaying passengers. Mary knew she would not be able to sleep, so when she saw that the Coriscan woman's thin garment was soaked, she put her own thick rug and shawl over the sleeper.

Sitting up all night had its rewards. She wrote of that night, "The mist comes stretching out from under the bushes over the sand toward the sea, now raising itself up into peaks, now crouching down upon the sand, and sending out long white arms or feelers towards the surf and then drawing them back as if it were some spirit-possessed thing, poisonous and malignant, that wanted to reach us . . . It . . . comes curling out in a white wall and during the rest of the calm before the dawn wind comes, wraps itself around us . . ."

It was not her first experience with mist. She had walked through it for miles in the forest while it hid the path at her feet and swished and swirled around her skirts. "I have seen it come out of the forests and gather on the creek before and round me when out o' nights in canoes," she wrote in her travel diary, "gradually, as we glided toward the breeze-swept river, forming itself into a great ball which has rolled before us, alongside, or behind us, showing dimly now in the shadow, ghostly white now in the moonshine, and bursting into thousands of flakes if the river breeze when it met it was too strong for it . . . Now and again you will see it in the forest stretch up a gradually lengthening arm, and wind it lazily around some grand column of a tree-stem . . . I have often played with it, scooping it up in my hands and letting it fall again, or swished it about with a branch, when it lay three or four feet from the ground . . ."

After a few other difficulties, the *Lafayette* landed again at Gaboon and was returned to Dr. Nassau. Saying her thank you and good-by to the aging man and to the other friends she had made in Gaboon, Mary headed for the Cameroons, her first stop on the long journey home. Traveling on the S.S. *Niger*, commanded by Captain Davies, she arrived at Victoria in Ambas Bay in September. Her crates of bottled fishes had already been sent home to the British Museum, and other shipments of fetish articles had gone to her brother's flat in Kensington. Soon she, too, would be in England—and she was not filled with anticipation at the thought. From where she stood on the deck of the *Niger* she could see one of her favorite mountains, the great peak of the Cameroons, Mungo Mah Lobeh, known as the "Throne of Thunder." On her first journey she had promised herself to come back someday and climb it, but . . . She let her gaze range over the towering pinnacles. The Cameroons, too, were Africa. If she climbed them she would have one more adventure, one more memory, and perhaps a bit of additional knowledge, to take back with her to warm her spirit during the cold, gray, English winter.

She turned to a fellow passenger. "Any fish up on those peaks?" she asked him.

The man turned to look curiously at her. He had heard about this woman scientist who had gone gallivanting all around cannibal country. He said, "I doubt it, miss. You'd better get your fish someplace safer, anyhow."

Mary smiled. She had not been serious. There would not be fish on top of the Throne. There were not even enough natives living on its steep slopes to provide any study of fetish. What possible excuse could she think of for climbing a mountain 13,760 feet high? She, who all of her life had been afraid to walk on the edge of any precipice! She would not be able to get anyone to guide her; Africans did not care any more for cool mountain air than she did. Mah Lobeh was the highest peak on the western side of the continent and one of the highest points in all Africa. It was no place for Mary—but looking at mountains from below was only half a loaf. She wanted to climb up there and see whatever was to be seen.

The ship was dropping anchor and Mary went to her cabin. As soon as she could, she would find Captain Davies and ask how to go about assembling a small expedition to climb the great peak.

❧ CHAPTER THIRTEEN

WITH THE HELP OF THE GERMAN AUTHORITIES AT VICTORIA, Mary was able to hire a small party of natives to act as guides and porters on an ascent of the Cameroons. The general spirit and physical calibre of her crew did not compare with that of her Fan friends, she noted. These coast dwellers were afraid of the spirit that they believed reigned over the great peak of Mungo Mah Lobeh.

Uneasy but not discouraged, Mary started out with her crew from Victoria on the morning of September 20, 1895. The weather was superb. At the bridge crossing the Lukole River, Mary said good-by to Herr Von Lucke, the German who had arranged for her expedition. She pointed at the sky and the sun-bathed foothills of the mountain. "See, I'm in luck."

"Today, maybe," Herr Von Lucke said skeptically. "The weather is not to be trusted, especially at tornado time. The Throne is the birthplace of tornadoes, you might say. Also, remember that you are climbing a way that has never been climbed before because it is considered so dangerous."

"I have no choice as to weather," Mary said. "I have to climb now or not at all, because I ought to be on my way home." She had deliberately chosen to make her ascent on the southeast slope, not because it was dangerous, but because she hoped to see uncharted mountain areas from that side.

The first part of the climb followed a new road being constructed by a German engineer, most of it an unfinished jumble of broken rocks and blasted trees. Mary picked her way around the worst boulders, keeping an eye on the scenery at the same time. On the banks of the road were tropical shrubs and ferns, behind which rose the familiar walls of the African forest wearing their decorations of brilliant climbing plants. The foothills were a soft, dark blue. Ahead of her and around her flew brilliant blue butterflies, flashing against the rich, brown earth.

A shadow went over the sun, and before the travelers reached the end of the road, rain was driving against them. Their route led them from the road onto a forest path that was so slippery and narrow they could hardly stay on their feet. The path brought them to where a mountain stream rushed down over reddish rocks in a cloud of foam, and Mary sighed. One more wading expedition, she thought, as the water swished around her boots. She had long ago lost count of the streams she had crossed in this manner.

When she came out on the other side of the stream, the rain had intensified. She could see only a few feet ahead and her men were dim figures moving through the downpour. It was like being in a ghost forest. Dripping phantoms, great palms and redwoods rose up in the mist before the sloshing party. There was just enough light to show the delicate green and gold of the mosses that covered the rocks at the edge of the path.

Swimming would be a better name for what they were doing than walking, Mary thought as they went on. Rain poured down inside her shoes, splashed against her face and trickled down inside the collar of her dress. In some places the grass grew higher than her head and each blade was a faucet leaking down on her.

The group had a chance to dry out somewhat that night, in the home of an African mission school teacher, but rain was still falling hard the next day when they started out once more. Looking in what she believed was the direction of the sea, Mary thought wistfully of the excellent view she might have had in clear weather. As it was, it was like looking out from the inside of a custard pudding.

To her surprise, her men remained cheerful. They slipped and fell in torrents and mud slides but regained their feet quickly and went on, singing. Perhaps she had misjudged them, she thought.

The path led through banks of bergamot and balsam and Mary drew in deep breaths of the wet, spicily fragrant air. When they came to a ravine with several pools of water in it she remembered her joke about collecting fishes on Mungo Mah Lobeh. But the joke was not as funny as she had thought, for there in the pools were fish!

"We go for stop here, Bum," she said to the leader of the men. "I catch fish, two, three, maybe more, put them in bottles, see?" She held up one of her fish-collecting containers.

Bum told the others to halt, also, and knelt beside her at the edge of one of the pools. Mary got out a small net and captured two interesting little fish and some water spiders. The temperature of the air in this particular spot was more even, without the extremes of hot and cold they had suffered the day before. Probably about seventy degrees, Mary estimated. As she put the fishes into their bottles and stowed the bottles away in the bag carried by one of the porters, she wished that one of her botanist friends in England could have been there with her. The soil was very rich and all around her was, besides the bergamot, native indigo with its underleaf of dark blue, and beautiful red and green coleuses.

At Buea, a gray-eyed German officer named Liebert was building himself a house. He offered the half-finished structure to Mary for the night, showing her into his own room. In it were a washstand and water and a real bed with a mattress! Quite a change, Mary thought gratefully, from the wooden benches she had slept on in the Fan villages.

She had an excellent night's rest and the next day was clear. Waking at five, Mary was eager to be on her way up the mountain. She got up and dressed and went to hunt up the cook of her expedition.

At her firm knock, he came to the door of the hut where he and some of the others were sleeping, yawning widely.

"Is chop ready?" Mary asked crisply. He was supposed to have served her breakfast at five, according to their agreement. "We start one time quick for peak. You tell the others to hurry."

She went back to Herr Liebert's house to wait, and after a while Kefalla, one of her party, showed up. "You no sabe this be Sunday, ma?" he asked reproachfully, his face trying to show how shocked he was.

"I sabe," Mary said calmly. None of the men were Christians and Sunday was not a holy day for them. She knew what was up. If she let them stay over in Buea all day, with nothing to do, some of them would get drunk on rum. It was hardly a way to keep the Sabbath, and anyway she had to get on with the climb if she was to stay on schedule.

Kefalla scratched his head, obviously trying to think of some more clinching argument. By that time Bum arrived, looking sleepy but making no objections to Mary's plans. She was giving him instructions about the baggage and provisions when Kefalla interrupted. "Dem men say dey sick. And Bobo got hot foot. No can climb mountain with hot foot."

Exasperated, Mary tried to think how to cope with this malingering on the part of her men. Herr Liebert was coming down the road and she told him what Kefalla had said.

"Of course they're stalling," he agreed, "but you might as well send the 'sick' ones back down. They'll only cause trouble for you. I can let you have some of my workmen as substitutes."

Mary accepted his offer with relief, giving the complaining men and boys orders for goods on the Victoria trading post in payment for their services so far, and taking on Herr Liebert's men in their place. One of the new men, Sasu, had gone up the big peak with an earlier party and would act as guide for her.

Again the fair weather deserted them as soon as the day had got well along. Striking through a new forest belt with the mist curling around the moss-covered tree trunks, Mary was distracted from her admiration of patches of satiny begonia leaves and clumps of tree ferns by the cook's plucking at her sleeve. "Ah no climb high," he announced flatly. "I go for town quick quick." He puffed with exaggerated breaths.

"Oh, come along, now. We'll soon be out of this hard part," Mary encouraged him. She could not afford to lose the cook, of all people. She frowned sternly at him.

"No like climbing." But Cook's voice was less firm as he stole a look at Mary. He finally picked up his load and began moving again.

Mary wondered just how many helpers she would have by the time, if ever, she reached the top of the Throne. Xenia, one of the men she had obtained from Liebert, was an excellent worker but was very queer-acting. She thought he did not have quite all his wits. As for Kefalla, he was both lazy and tiresome, talking constantly until her ears rang.

Well, she promised herself, she was going to the top if she had to go all alone.

With increasing altitude, the vegetation began to thin out. The trees wore greenish-white lichen trim instead of the deeper-colored moss. The travelers made camp in the middle of a downpour, stretching a canvas sheet from four pegs to make a canopy. Mary ate a quick meal of canned pork and herring and then set out to see what lay ahead before the daylight was gone. Climbing through jungle grass up a steep and slippery mound, she found herself face to face with the steep wall of the mountain, behind which must be the peak itself. She took out her compass to get her bearings, meantime searching the mountain's face for the easiest way to climb it. A shout from the men warned her that darkness was descending and she had to go back to the camp. By the time she reached the welcome warmth of the camp fire, it was time to light her own lantern and crawl onto the camp bed the men had put up for her some twenty feet from their own rough beds. There would be just time to make a few notes in her travel journal before going to sleep. She lifted her head, listening with a familiar ache of pleasure. Somewhere a bird whistled in a deep, rich tone.

So far, despite the rain, the trip had gone reasonably well, at least to such a seasoned traveler as Mary had become, but disaster was waiting.

At the next water hole Monrovia Boy, the most trusted of Mary's crew, went down the surrounding rocks to fill their various containers. He had barely reached his goal when he called back, "Water no live here, ma."

No water! Jolted by this unexpected news, Mary tried to show no concern. "Well, we'll just have to get along with what we have in our extra jugs," she said cheerfully.

Sasu, the guide, looked down at his toes. "No live in jugs, either," he said bluntly. "Water no live us at all." He lifted one of the canteens and tipped it up to show her how empty it was.

Mary looked from one to the other of the men, her eyes narrowing. It was very odd, she thought, that none of the men had mentioned how low their water supply was. They must have known how much would be needed, when they left Buea and Herr Liebert's headquarters.

"Men cannot climb mountains without water," Kefalla said slyly. "No more water holes this side of mountain."

They thought she would give up the climb and go back to Victoria, Mary realized. That was why they had been so cheerful earlier. They had reasoned, probably because she was a woman, that she should have given up before this, but since she hadn't, they were going to force her into it. They didn't know this "ma," she said to herself.

She scolded them soundly, calling them bad men. Then she called down to Monrovia Boy that he should come up quick quick. When the young man had caught his breath, she gave him a note she had scribbled for Herr Liebert requesting some bottled water. "Take this back to Buea," she said, hoping her trust in Monrovia Boy was not misplaced. She told the men that when Monrovia Boy returned with the water, they were to bring it to a new camp at the top of the mountain wall.

Mary began to climb again, turning her back on her cowardly companions. Above the scratching of her shoes on the rock wall, she listened for some sound of footsteps behind her. They did not all need to wait for the return of the water.

Pausing at last for breath, she glanced back. The sullen-faced crew stood below where she had left them, except for two men. The half-crazy Xenia and one other were toiling up the slope toward her. Part-way up, the second man stopped and Xenia came on alone, Mary's large, black bag in his hand. In the bag was a small bottle of sour claret. Seeking shade from the now blazing sun in the shelter of a rock, Mary and Xenia shared the claret as the only relief for their thirst.

"You come now quick," Mary said when they had rested. She was anxious to go on.

Xenia cast a nervous look upward. "My foot be tired too much," he said, and slumped back under the rock.

Mary decided not to waste time arguing with him and went on alone. Blasts of wind struck her face, a hot wind that brought no relief from the sun. Every rock was an oven. Only a few sad-looking bushes grew among the rocks, one with a roselike yellow flower, sedum plants with pink-white blooms, a silvery-leaved herb, and a large green orchid.

Reaching the shelf of the rock wall, she stopped to rest. Fighting off dizziness, she forced herself to peer over the shelf's edge at the panorama of lower mountains, mangrove swamps, bright rivers and mile on mile of lush, tropical bloom. It seemed that she could see all of Africa spread out before her. Closer by was the vast crater of Mungo, its fires slumbering now. Shivering in the sharp wind, she almost wished the volcano would throw off some heat, or that she could have preserved the heat of the earlier part of the climb. In one of the chasms of a mountain below, a thunderstorm was brewing.

The shadows were long and dusk would come soon. She would never be able to reach the peak today.

Mists rose around her as she picked her way downward to where she had left her men. She hoped that Monrovia Boy had come back with the water and she would find camp all made and food cooking. Suddenly, out of the mist appeared Xenia, too lost and frightened to be scolded for moving from the spot where she had left him. Mary urged him gently along with her back down the slope.

There was no one in the spot where she had last seen the men; there was only an empty soda-water syphon bottle. Mary, her lips parched and bleeding, her face raw from wind and sun, felt anger explode in her. Searching her pocket for the small revolver she had brought with her, she fired several shots into the air. The echoes had scarcely died away when she heard answering yells. Following the voices, she found the camp that the men had established.

They faced her guiltily, each one outdoing the other in an attempt to explain their cowardice. Each speaker insisted that it was not he but some other person in the party who "got fright too much."

Monrovia Boy had not returned with the water. There was no food. The cook had taken all their beef and rice back to Buea to be cooked because he had no water to cook it in.

Mary closed her eyes in weary despair. There was nothing to do but wait.

A few days later, on September 26, Mary Kingsley made the final ascent of the great peak of the Cameroons, alone. In bitter wind and stinging rain, she reached the cairn built by the Germans who had climbed the mountain some years before by a different path. Adding a few rocks to the cairn to honor the magnificent mountain, she turned away but after a moment crept back through the mist.

It was only civil to leave one's calling card when making a call, she thought, smiling at her own whimsy. Fishing hers out from the bag on her arm, she wedged the white, engraved square of paper in among the stones of the cairn. Mungo would soon make pulp of it but the gesture pleased her just the same.

Looking down at that symbol of civilization gleaming among the rugged stones, she was keenly aware that very soon she would be on her way back to England. When or how she would return to Africa, she did not know, but somehow, some day, she must. In the meantime, she would do all she could to make her adventures and research and hardships count for something, to England and the world. With this hope sustaining her, she faced the cold wind and the loose cinders and lava that covered her downward path. Mary Kingsley was the twenty-eighth person known to have ascended the highest peak of the Cameroons, but she was the first ever to climb it from the southeast, or more difficult and dangerous side.

🌿 CHAPTER FOURTEEN

THE LECTURE HALL IN DUNDEE, SCOTLAND, WAS ALREADY filled to capacity but still more people crowded in as Mary Kingsley walked onto the platform. Her face was drawn with cold and fatigue and her gray-blue eyes were troubled. The chest cold that had been bothering her was a little better but she had another one of her dreadful headaches. She fingered the high, stiff black collar of her dress as though to pull it back from her throat, and wondered vaguely if her hat was on straight. Her brother Charles had said, the last time he saw her lecture, that the ornamental pins on top of her hat had leaned to the right. She had always found bothering about clothes very tiresome—it had been so simple just to wear her black skirts and blouses in the jungle—but she did not want to disgrace Charles or her friends now that she was in the public eye.

All this business of gloves and rings and posies—how the Fan ladies would have loved it! Which only proved that the human race was not as easily divided into this or that classification, after all. Thinking of the Fans brought a rush of longing for Africa. Mary had not expected to be still in England in November, 1899, almost three years after her return from the tropics. Two months ago she had made definite plans to go out again, for a third trip, but she had been talked out of it.

"England needs you, Mary," Sir George Goldie, head of

the Niger Company, had told her. "You can't run away to your precious swamps and moonlight boat trips in the middle of the fight."

Mary, looking out over the assorted faces of her audience, wondered. The "fight" often seemed a losing one. She had tried, ever since she came back, to make the English people understand the African peoples. She had given lectures in every corner of the British Isles, had written letters and articles for every publication interested in Africa, had published three books about her own experiences and research, and in addition had kept up a fighting correspondence with England's statesmen on the subject. She was tired, tired, tired. But still, one kept on fighting.

"Ladies and gentlemen," she began, looking into the faces of the people in the front rows, "I don't know what you have been reading in the papers about me but whatever it is, it's probably not true. I was not made a cannibal chief, nor did I cross the continent of Africa alone and unguided."

A few smiles and chuckles told Mary that her audience had read some of the wilder stories about her exploits. They had also, she thought grimly, probably read what she thought of the hut-tax which the English government was trying to impose on the Africans. Well, they would hear it again. And again and again. She launched into her lecture, describing first some of her choicest adventures on the Ogowé and Rembwé Rivers, and then explaining why the tax on African homes in British-administered Africa had caused so much bloodshed and trouble.

"African law has a basic principle," she said. "That is, that if you pay someone else money for living on a property, it is not your property. That's how the African feels about the hut-tax. He built his hut himself and he considers it almost his most valuable possession—except for his wives."

A ripple went through the audience and Mary noted an older woman in the second row leaning over to mumble to her companion.

She's probably saying, "See, they're absolute heathens, those Africans, and the sooner we lick them into shape, the better," Mary thought.

She took a good breath and went on. "Remember, England did not *conquer* the territories she supervises in Africa; she got her chance there by agreement with native chiefs. We therefore have no right to force our taxes, our laws, and our beliefs down Africa's throat. If we are to help—and I want England to stay in Africa and help my dark-skinned friends there—it must be done by working through their own laws and customs."

Some of the faces below her were shocked, some dismayed, some amused, and many doubtful. Surely they must care, Mary told herself as she talked on. They must see that we cannot simply exploit the Africans, that we must supervise their growth and improvement with honor and justice.

The applause, when she finished, was enthusiastic. The head of the society that was sponsoring the lecture presented her with a bouquet of flowers.

"I am very honored, sir." Mary bowed first to him and then to the audience, trying not to look at the bouquet. Ants were crawling over the flowers. The Scottish ant was probably harmless, but after Africa she looked with some anxiety at any ant.

From Dundee, Mary's tour would take her to Edinburgh and then on to other Scottish towns. She wished it were over and that she could go back to London. Charley had been sick when she left and she was, as usual, worried about him.

When she arrived home, Mary found that her brother

was better. "I suppose it was that old lung trouble again," she said to him as they sat down to supper together after her return.

"Günther sent a message around to you," Charles said. He helped himself to a slice of beef. "Wants to know why you haven't been down to help lately. It seems he has a lot of fish rotting on his hands in the Museum." Charles laughed, his eyes twinkling affectionately across the table at Mary.

"I'll go down next week. Of course Günther thinks I should give up the lectures and the politics and all that, and just settle down to studying his blessed fishes." Mary let her shoulders drop suddenly, as though the idea were a tempting one. "Will you really go off to China again, Charley, when you keep having these colds?"

"Will you really go off to Africa again, Mary, when you keep having these colds?" he mocked her. "Listen to you! You've been wheezing and sneezing since the day your ship landed, but I don't see you slowing down any. Of course I'm off to China—first chance I get. Let's stop this and talk about something else. By the way, I finished that new book on the East today. It's excellent. I hope you'll have a chance to read it soon."

Mary thought of the pile of correspondence on her desk, of the household duties that seemed to pile up whenever she was away on a lecture tour despite the help of Martha, the housekeeper. There were still fetish objects from African tribes that had never been thoroughly described in any of her writings. Then there was the introduction to her father's book *Notes and Memoirs of a Sportsman* which Charley was supposed to be working at but never seemed to do. She had about finished that, though. *The Story of West Africa*, a small history of those colonies she had visited, and which

178

she had been asked by a publisher to compile, was to be published early next year.

The housekeeper came in and Mary said, "We'll have our coffee in by the fire, Martha. This room is chilly."

"Yes, Miss Kingsley."

Charles had a favorite chair near the fire in the parlor. As he sank down into it, he took up the newspaper on the table beside the chair.

Mary, presiding over the coffee pot, looked over at him as he opened the paper. "What's the news?" she asked anxiously. She meant the news about the Boer War. Things had been going badly for the British in South Africa. The Boers, who were Dutch Africans, were better equipped and very determined to get the British out of the Orange Free State and the Transvaal.

"Depressing," Charles said grimly. He handed her the paper. "Here, read it yourself."

Mary gave him his coffee and sat down on a settee to read the account of the war's progress. All afternoon she had been feeling an increased tension, as though her life was somehow going in the wrong direction. She wanted to look after Charles, but he didn't really let her. Anyway, he was going away again by summer. She had almost written and talked herself out on West Africa. Lately there had been too many parties where she had had to wear fancy clothes and try to behave like a distinguished personage when no one knew better than she did that she was only herself. In Africa, when she came out of a trip into the bush, all mud and fish smell and bitten by bugs, with her hair falling down, the traders would shout, "Who is it?" before letting her on their property.

"It's only me," she had always answered.

So they had given her the nickname "Only Me." Well,

Only Me was getting badly lost in London's philosophical circles, she felt.

"I've got to go out there, Charley," she said suddenly, putting down the paper.

He frowned. "To the Coast?"

"No. To South Africa. To help with the war."

Her brother snorted. "What kind of help? They don't take women soldiers. They have to let them have the vote before they can give them guns."

"Women don't need votes. They'll just complicate politics if they ever do get the vote. There is plenty of real work for real women in the world without their messing with politics. No, Charley, I don't want a gun—nasty things, guns. But I do want to help."

He sighed. "I wish I had your energy."

Later, alone in her bedroom, Mary tossed and turned, unable to sleep. What good had been done by all her writing and lecturing, her letters to the *Times* and other publications, her travels from one end of England to the other? The tax on the natives' homes would remain. She had argued in favor of the traders and the information and understanding they would be able to give the government, but the traders were still considered a rough lot concerned mainly with making a profit from liquor. She had argued against some of the missionaries because she sincerely believed they were shortsighted in their views—and ended by wounding one of the best of them, Dennis Kemp, her friend. She had tried to show Africa's heart and soul, as she understood it, to her countrymen, but she was greatly afraid that most of them still considered the Negroes and Bantus very little more than animals. The year before, her dearly beloved friend, Lady Goldie, wife of Sir George Taubman Goldie of the Royal Niger Company, had died. Mary herself had been very, very ill and was more often sick than well. Last and not least—even alone in her room, Mary could scarcely think about it—she had fallen in love with a man who, wonderful though he was, had felt not the least return of her interest in him.

The man was Major Matthew Nathan, later to become Sir Matthew Nathan, administrator of Sierra Leone in West Africa. He was Jewish and Mary had always liked Jewish people, because of, in her own words, "their dreamy minds, their hard common sense and their love of beautiful material objects." It was sad that the one man she had ever cared for in a romantic fashion was unable to return her love.

She got out of bed, turned on a light, and picked up a book by Joseph Conrad. She never tired of reading him even though she seldom liked fiction. Conrad was one writer who shared both her love of the sea and her desire for adventure. But even Conrad could not hold her attention that night. The old profound melancholy of those days which followed the death of her father and mother came swooping back on her. She was useless in England. There was nothing important left here for her to do, nothing to stir her mind and test her courage.

She had spoken only half-seriously to her brother about going out to South Africa, but as she fought melancholy and fatigue her resolve hardened. She would offer to serve as a nurse in the Boer War. It was not her beloved West Coast but it was Africa.

At first Mary's offer to go out to Africa as a nurse was refused. The war, said the War Office, would soon be over. But by February, 1900, it was evident that the Boers had settled in for a real fight, and Mary was asked to go out as soon as she could.

The *Moor*, which carried her to South Africa, left England the first week in March. On board ship with her were some seven hundred men and officers of the British military, some of whom became ill when they reached the tropics so that Mary's nursing duties began before she ever reached her destination. Stepping out onto the deck for a breath of air one night after helping to check the fever of a soldier, she looked up at the soft, dark sky with a feeling of mixed happiness and pain. She was, at last, "homeward" bound to her beloved Africa, but not, as she had so long dreamed of doing, to go skylarking about in those wildly beautiful rivers and forests near the west coast which she so dearly loved. She was going now to sickness and death, to do one more of the "odd jobs" with which the thirty-eight years of her life had mostly been filled.

A brief stop at Cape Town brought her one pleasure, however. She had long been an admirer of Rudyard Kipling, even though she disagreed with him in some of his statements about the so-called "white man's burden." She met both him and Mrs. Kipling at Cape Town.

But there was very little time to develop such friendship. Mary reported to General Wilson at the military headquarters as soon as she could after landing.

"What can I do?" she asked.

The tired general looked at this frail-appearing woman with considerable doubt and some disapproval. "What if I asked you to go to Simonstown to nurse Boers?" he asked.

"Whatever you say, sir." Mary had done things considerably more difficult than to go to a small hospital and nurse prisoners. She thought of the infected wounds and dreadful sores she had cleaned and treated in the Fan villages.

"All right. I'll arrange your passage. God knows you're needed."

The words were not spoken irreverently, Mary realized when she reached the Palace Hospital at Simonstown. The Boer prisoners were having an epidemic of enteric fever and measles. There were only two other nurses when she arrived, and one doctor. The hospital had two floors, divided into wards on each floor, full of bugs and lice and crowded with prisoners. The British had supplied plenty of food and medicines but had hardly anyone to give them out.

"Miss Johanna, Miss Johanna, oh please, Miss Johanna!" wailed a boy on one of the narrow iron cots that crowded the wards, as Mary made her rounds in early evening of a Sunday in April. He had been crying out like that for the past twenty-four hours and Mary, feeling helpless, went for the tenth time to his side. She took his hand and murmured, "Yes, dear. Yes, yes. Here I am."

It did no good. He continued to toss and moan and cry out. She moved on, past a prisoner who reached out for her skirt as she passed his cot. "Pants," he gasped out. "Where my pants iss?"

The man's trousers were probably piled up with the clothing of other infected prisoners, in a yard behind the hospital. But she said, "I'll find out," as she had over and over to the men who inquired, either about their clothing or their families or their money or whatever else disturbed their feverish dreams.

On the ground floor she ran into Doctor Carré.

"We're getting another nurse and a second doctor," he told her, looking jubilant in spite of the circles under his eyes. "How many went tonight?"

"Five." That was two less than the day before, Mary comforted herself. Death was the real ruler of this place and both she and the good doctor fought death here as in England she had fought the ideas she thought so wrong, about the African people. It was an exhausting battle.

"That man upstairs, the big one in the corner," she said, leaning wearily against the wall, "keeps yelling '*Ons land! Ons land!*' even in his sleep. Today when he was awake he described to me every hill and river bend and twist of the road in what he considers his own country."

"The Boers are fanatics on the subject," Doctor Carré answered. "They've forgotten that the land belonged first to the dark-skinned Africans; they think of it as having been theirs for thousands of years."

English people in empire lands made the same mistake, Mary thought. The truth was that almost all habitable land in the world *was* owned by someone, before the white man came to occupy it in his own name. She dismissed her own thoughts impatiently; this was no time for reflection.

"With an additional doctor, I suppose that means you won't be here all the time," she said. "I hope you'll get more rest."

He raised his eyebrows at her. "I'll get as much as you're getting, Miss Mary, and you know how little that is." He laid a warning hand on her shoulder. "Try to take care of yourself."

It was good advice, Mary thought, as she moved away toward a beckoning patient, but since she had never spent much time taking care of herself it was probably too late to begin. Bending over the sick soldier, moistening his hot mouth and forehead with a cool cloth, it seemed that she was back years in time. Brushing her wrist against her own damp forehead, she closed her eyes, hearing again the voices she had grown up with, voices that had demanded or requested some service from her.

"I'm coming . . . Yes, I'll be there in a moment . . . Of course, you can have some water . . . There, now, I'll brew you some tea."

Under her fatigue she felt a strange, stinging gratitude for the opportunity she had in this bitter place. Every resource of her body and imagination was challenged here. She thanked God for such strength as she had, bracing herself against the death staring at her from one young prisoner's face. This was a desperate game, with so many other lives at stake.

A month later, Mary felt the first, sudden onslaught of serious sickness. Defiantly, she tried to shake off the pains and fever that gripped her, but the lines of her face were drawn and the flush on her cheeks was too unnatural to conceal.

"I insist on taking your temperature," one of the new nurses, Nurse Rae, told her.

"Its only a touch of West Coast fever; nothing to worry about." She'd had fever many times, in the Congo, and had conquered it, Mary thought.

Nurse Rae forced the thermometer into Mary's mouth. When she drew it out again, she exclaimed, "A touch of fever, indeed! You'd better get into bed at once."

Weakly, Mary let herself be put to bed.

"I'll catch the doctor as soon as he comes and have him take a look at you," Nurse Rae said, plumping a pillow.

"Don't send the doctor yet," Mary said, gasping against a fresh jab of pain. "Wait until tomorrow, when Dr. Carré will be on duty again. Go look after your real patients. I'll be all right here."

Another wave of pain washed over her as the nurse left. The pain and the fever made her feel giddy. Half delirious, she pushed herself up on her elbow, imagining that just beyond the door a circle of Fans stood, robed in the outlandish, weird garments of monkey hunters. "No, no, sah," they cried. "No white sah watch; scare big monkeys away." Then, suddenly, one of the large-eyed, full-lipped hunters ran forward, holding out his hand, smiling. "You big spirit. We welcome you!"

The pain ebbed. She lay back, staring up at the ceiling. My friends, she thought. The Fans, Igalwas, Krumen, traders, missionaries . . . The medicinal odors evaporated. She breathed deeply, dreaming that once again she stood on a little river steamer, gliding past banks of fragrant flowers, watching clouds rear steeply up behind the endless African forests.

She was only vaguely aware, much later, of Dr. Carré standing over her, Nurse Rae beside him.

He examined her and shook his head at the nurse. "Perforation of the lower intestine," he said. "We'll have to try operating."

Mary opened her eyes and said clearly and calmly, "Send a telegram to my brother. I think he's still in London."

"Yes, yes, I will," the doctor said. He was looking at her with worried, sorrowful eyes.

The operation came too late. When Mary returned to consciousness following it, she saw in the stricken faces of her fellow-workers that Africa had, at last, been too much for her. A trembling smile came to her lips. "The animals," she said, "are allowed to be alone when they die. Please give me the same privilege, my very good friends."

Nurse Rae beckoned to the others. To Mary she said, "We'll leave the door open. If you want us, just call."

Mary nodded, her eyelids drooping with weakness. When they were gone, she turned on her side, slowly, so she could look out the window. It was already growing dark outside. Perhaps in a moment she would see the great purple night gather in the sky again, and the immense planets turning slowly in their course. Why, it was already night! And there was a golden river, and thousands of silver fish leaping. How wide and radiant the circles were where they splashed! And how refreshing the air blowing in from the strange, foaming ocean . . . She sank back on her pillow, smiling.

Before Charles Kingsley could sail for the Cape in response to Dr. Carré's telegram which arrived June 3, 1900, his sister Mary was dead. She had made only one final request, which was that she be buried at sea. Sir Alfred Jones, a wealthy Liverpool shipowner and a good friend of Mary's, was to be asked to see to fulfilling this request, but it was not left to Sir Alfred. Mary's native country, England, recognized what she had given it during the eight years of her life which followed her parents' death. Mary was buried with full military and naval honors in the bay at Simonstown on the Cape of Good Hope.

Many were the tributes paid to Mary Kingsley, then and later. A friend, E. D. Morel, wrote in the *British Empire Review*, "As she lived, so she died, doing good to the end." And later, in an introduction to a book on Africa, he said, "Few women . . . have inspired all sorts and conditions of men with so intense a respect, so wondering an admiration . . . as Mary Kingsley. She was so unassuming, so unaffected . . . The truest, kindest, staunchest friend that ever breathed . . ."

Sir George Goldie said that she had the brain of a man

and the heart of a woman. John Holt, head of one of England's largest trading companies in Africa, wrote, ten years after her death, "Just look what Mary Kingsley did for us all. She gave us credit for having some kind of human charity in our hearts, of having some good in us, and what endless trouble she gave herself to bring it out of us."

These tributes, given to a woman who claimed to prefer nonhuman things like swamp, moonlight and mist, might seem strange, except that Mary Kingsley's acts belied her words. Much as she loved the landscape of Africa, she concerned herself more with its people. In her last lecture before going to Simonstown, she gave a final warning: ". . . the finest of all African races, the true Negroes, whose homeland is in West Africa from Gambia to Cameroon, can be made as loyal and devoted to England as the man in the street up here, provided you do not make . . . mistakes in dealing with him today."

If England has not made as many mistakes, perhaps, as other European powers, particularly Belgium, some part of the credit must surely go to Mary Kingsley.

Dr. Carré, in writing to Sir Alfred Jones about the last weeks of Mary Kingsley's life, said, "She was a thoroughly good woman with a giant intellect. We could not afford to lose her but we have."

No one who contributed what Mary Kingsley did to the world is truly lost. Her writings are few—three books, some magazine and newspaper articles, and private letters. All are charged with the richness of her spirit, her unfailing humor, her courage, and her talent for description. Her *West African Studies* is a major contribution to the understanding of tribal fetish, laws and customs, and her *Travels in West Africa* on which most of this book is based, combines information, adventure and literary style to create a remarkable book for anyone to have written—almost unbelievable from one who had no formal education. She did not write a great deal about the fish she went to such trouble to collect, but three species of fish were named for her and her collections are prized by the British Museum.

Having fish species named for her pleased Mary Kingsley. She would have been even more pleased with the memorial created by her friends and fellow scientists, which is the Royal African Society founded in her honor. On the title page of each issue of this society's journal is a reproduction of a small portrait medallion of Mary. In addition to this tribute, a Mary Kingsley medal for research into tropical diseases is given at the Liverpool School of Tropical Medicines.

Mary Kingsley's real contributions, however, as with all men and women of genius and original thought, cannot be measured by medals or memorials. She once wrote, "The Negroes are a great world race, a race not passing off the stage of affairs, but one that has an immense amount of history before it." In this she was surely a prophet.

Brought up to be little more than a servant, messenger and secretary in a household dominated by her father, in a time when women, even with a husband and family, scarcely ventured beyond the confines of their homes, Mary Kingsley set out alone at thirty-two to find something to do with her life, something that would make it, and the life of humanity, more worthwhile. Humility, fearlessness, and sympathetic imagination brought her a triumph far beyond what she had ever hoped for.

Perhaps, if her friends the Fans and the other native Africans whom she had scolded, admired, traded with, nursed through sores, fever and epidemic—listening always to what they said with the keenest interest and with infinite patience—had expressed their feelings about Mary Kingsley's efforts in and for Africa, they might have put it like this: "Bery fine ting, ma! You do plenty plenty."

That tribute would have given Mary Kingsley deep pleasure. It was for her friends the Africans that she had fought on the lecture platforms and in the newspapers and in her books. For them and the white man who had blundered into their world. As long as her books are read, as they are today in anthropology classes and by students of Africa, what she had to say carries on the mission for understanding between black man and white that she followed devotedly in person while she lived.